A PLAY BY JOHN TOWNSEND

Ski Jump

Non-fiction section by
Christopher Edge

PEARSON

Published by Pearson Education Limited, Edinburgh Gate,
Harlow, Essex, CM20 2JE.

www.pearsonschoolsandfecolleges.co.uk

Play text © John Townsend 2012
Non-fiction text © Christopher Edge
Typeset by Phoenix Photosetting, Chatham, Kent, UK
Cover photo © PhotoDisc/Getty Images

The rights of John Townsend and C.E. to be identified as authors of this work has
been asserted by them in accordance with the Copyright, Designs and Patents
Act 1988.

First published 2012

16 15 14 13 12
11 10 9 8 7 6 5 4 3 2 1

British Library Cataloguing in Publication Data
A catalogue record for this book is available from the British Library.

ISBN 9780435075422

Printed in China (CTPS/01)

Acknowledgments
We would like to thank Biggar High School and students for their invaluable help
in the development and trialling of this book.

Contents

Act Two

Cast list

MAIN CHARACTERS

BRADLEY	Pupil in Year 9
KATIE	Bradley's friend – pupil in Year 9
HARJIT	Bradley's friend – pupil in Year 9
ADIOLA	Bradley's friend – pupil in Year 9
AJ	Bradley's friend – pupil in Year 10
MISS FARMER	Form teacher
MR MINHAS	Gymnastics teacher
DAD	Mr Stradling, Bradley's dad
LIPSTUD	Young man with a lip stud
GIRLFRIEND	His girlfriend
KARL	18-year-old German ski instructor

OTHER CHARACTERS

DOCTOR	
MEDIC 1, MEDIC 2	Two medical staff
MANDY	Air stewardess
STAFF	Airport staff
WAITRESS	Hotel waitress
STEVE	Coach driver

Staging suggestions

The way that any director or any cast approaches staging a play is bound to be only one way of looking at the text. Even the oldest plays are endlessly reinterpreted as we continue to find new ways of looking at them. Quite simply, there is no right or wrong way to stage a play, but there are ways which offer greater or lesser challenges to actors and audiences. These staging suggestions will depend more on developing a strong ensemble feel within your cast than they will on bulky and costly sets. As a theatre-goer, I feel the drama starts to die the moment a curtain closes and you hear the scenery trundling around, and it can take a long time to regain lost momentum. I always want the story and the characters to keep moving. I think audiences are happy to suspend disbelief and use their own imaginations if you reward them with a performance that has wit, charm, style and vision, even if you are working in a limited or limiting space.

Ski Jump has almost as much action as a Bourne movie or an Alex Rider novel so any director should try to keep the actors and audience breathless. The opening and final scenes take us full circle and can afford to be measured and unhurried, but from Act One, Scene 1, we need to feel like feet won't be touching the ground for a while.

As an overall approach, my suggestion is to keep this piece pacey, light on its feet and clean. The audience should always know where they are. Whatever the setting, it is the actors' words, expressions and gestures which convey meaning, so don't labour over sets which don't drive the tale on.

I would suggest the following:

Setting and costumes

- Use standard sized, pale-painted stage flats to delineate discrete areas of performance.
- Think about abandoning the stage for a flat floor if you have that option and spread the action around the audience to create a visual dynamic. Three or four performance areas would give you lots of scope.
- Consider using stage blocks to replicate tables, chairs, beds, etc. Once this convention is set up, the audience will relax into it and follow you into the world of the play. Try using actors playing smaller roles to move the blocks rather than having stage hands come in; it keeps the action going and keeps the story alive.

- I'm proposing fairly pared-back and stylised settings, but I would suggest keeping props and costumes very naturalistic to help root us in the play's extraordinary events.

Projection

In the last decade, projection has come into its own as a legitimate theatre design tool and I think it may be just what this piece needs. Simple projections of words and images will help the audience get a sense of where we are both in time and place. This doesn't need to be anything fancy, just efficient – almost as a movie caption would tell us that we are in 'London, England'.

Heartbeat

Taking your lead from the opening, perhaps create a heartbeat that plays as the audience enter. This can run through the hospital scene and cover any tricky transitions. Using it between the first few scenes and reprising it in Act Two should help to build tension and suspense. It might give the sense that we are reliving the patient's experience through their unconscious state, which is no bad thing.

I suggest that even before the play begins, the patient is centre, lying on blocks under a sheet, motionless and silent while people take their seats.

The locations that need to be defined in *Ski Jump* are as follows:

Act One	Act Two
• hospital • school (hall, corridor and changing room) • dry-ski slope • aeroplane • airport (arrivals and enquiry desk) • coach • motorway service station (two locations)	• mountain café • hotel (Bradley's room, lobby and dining room) • ski slopes • cable car • first aid chalet near ski lift station • the hospital from the Prologue

Prologue (p 1): Hospital

Heartbeat.

The hospital scene is a prologue. It can be played without any real setting. The dialogue, the beep and wheeze of medical machinery, the heartbeat and a couple of white coats will make any audience member know where we are. Actors rush on, they rush off, job done. As they exit, several 'neutral' actors (who play smaller parts) in plain grey/cream clothing enter and lift the patient from their bed.

Act One, Scene 1 (pp 3–12): Parents' evening

Heartbeat. Projected caption: 'Months earlier'.

Lights up on one of your performance areas. A sign is projected – 'St Paul's Community College (or similar) Parents' Evening'. A teacher sits below. The neutral actors place Bradley in the scene, then exit. The dialogue with his father starts and we are into the main tale.

Act One, Scene 2 (pp 13–14): School corridor

Heartbeat. Projected caption: 'A few days later'.

Shift to a new performance area. Sound of a bell and school hall voices. The cast enter as if on their way to the next class, deliver their lines and exit after their high five.

Act One, Scene 3 (pp 15–19): Dry-ski slope

Heartbeat. Projected caption: 'A few weeks later'.

On the next performance area a sign is projected – 'Milltown (or similar) Sports and Leisure Centre, Dry-ski Slope, Training Area'. Dispense with any thought of actually using skis – poles and acting will do. Have the actors raised on blocks to give them height. Their performance should tell us how high they are supposed to be and how cumbersome the skis are.

Act One, Scene 4 (pp 20–22): Aeroplane

As soon as the lights go down on the ski slope, begin playing the various airport announcements. I don't think we need anyone else to 'people' the scene. A simple jacket for Mandy and a block for the two passengers to sit on will suffice.

Act One, Scenes 5 and 6 (pp 23–32): Airport arrivals and enquiries

Both of the scenes in the airport can have the babble of passengers, occasional flight announcements and intermittent engine sounds under them. Use different areas for each and project airport-signage ('Arrivals' and 'Enquiries') to keep the audience clear as to exactly where we are. Use blocks for tables, chairs and desks.

I suggest setting up a single 'slow-motion' moment where Bradley delves into his bag and pulls out Lipstud's book. A change in sound and light to accentuate this will help. We'll use this convention again in Act Two, so be sure to use the same light and sound any time you go into slow motion.

Act One, Scene 7 (pp 33–36): School changing room

This scene is clearly set with the opening speech. If actors are drying hair, buttoning shirts, tying laces and ties, we will know exactly where we are.

Act One, Scene 8 (pp 37–40): Coach

Use the blocks to create coach seating, perhaps with a projection of landscape passing or light moving by to add some interest.

Act One, Scenes 9 and 10 (pp 41–48): Two locations in a motorway service station

Project images of typical service station shops and fast-food outlets across all your stage flats. These scenes take place across the whole service station and they are where the play begins to gear up. Play them expansively and use the whole space to make the audience feel almost surrounded by, and involved in, the action. Use your neutral actors to 'people' the scenes.

Act One, Final speeches (p 47–48)

As the final speeches of Act One are delivered, the neutral actors pick up Bradley and deliver him back to his hospital bed. They pull up a sheet and exit as Lipstud says, 'I've made up my mind – he must be eradicated.' Lights down.

Act Two

Act Two is almost exclusively set in Alpine spaces. Use fairly impressionistic washes of white and icy blue projected onto your flats as a default for this act.

Act Two, Scenes 1, 3, 4, 6: Mountain café and hotel lobby and dining room

- **Scene 1 (pp 49–52):** Simply use a sign and some blocks as tables and chairs to create the mountain café.
- **Scene 3 (pp 57–59):** Blocks, a waitress with a tray and a hotel bar sign will suffice for this very short scene.
- **Scene 4 (pp 60–65):** Spend time instead creating the dining room. Sound of gentle voices and cutlery will help create ambience. Turning the lobby into the dining room around Bradley, using the same performing area, will help make it feel like part of the same hotel.
- **Scene 6 (pp 70–72):** Revert back to the original mountain café setting, but with perhaps warmer evening lighting. Use the same performance space to recreate this scene to keep it firm in the audience's mind.

Act Two, Scene 2 (pp 53–56): Bradley's room

Bradley's hotel bedroom is created partly by the bed (made of blocks) but mostly by Mr Minhas' lines; we know his room is up high. When he heads out onto the balcony, a sound effect of occasional cars and chill wind will help the actor create a sense of height through gesture and facial expression. If Bradley is raised on a block and two neutral actors hold something as simple as a wooden pole to act as the balcony rail, when we see him cross it and ease himself down, we'll get a sense of his doing something risky.

Act Two, Scene 5 (pp 66–69): Ski slopes

This scene can be played very much like the dry-ski slope scene from earlier, except with the addition of the characters being *clearly cold*. Something as simple as blowing and rubbing hands will help create a sense of place.

Act Two, Scene 7 (pp 73–75): Gondola ski lift

Unless you have a massive budget and very well resourced theatre, forget about having the cable car go up and down. If you can arrange some blocks with a sturdy central pillar on a wheeled base and a frame to suggest the size and shape, you'll be doing well. Throughout the scene this can be gently moved and jostled by the neutral actors to indicate movement. The actors will have to indicate height through facial expressions.

Act Two, Scene 8 (pp 76–78): First aid chalet

For this scene use a 'Mountain First Aid' sign, sombre blue light, the sound of wind and of heavy machinery moving the cable cars. At this point, revert back to the slow-motion convention established in Act One, Scene 5 (remembering to use the same light and sound). Use your neutral actors to safely move, lift and place Karl as he falls from the wheelchair into the snow. If done cleanly and stylistically, this can have real drama and pathos.

Act Two, Scene 9 (pp 79–89): Cable car

This scene can take its time. It's full of exposition from Lipstud and reaction from Bradley. We need to see through Bradley's face how scary it is. A great deal happens right at the end of this scene and I suggest that it is played fairly naturalistically until Lipstud says 'Your time is up, kid...'.

At this point, revert back to the slow-motion convention established in Act One, Scene 5 (remembering to use the same light and sound). This will make it safer for the actor playing Bradley and clearer for the audience.

Big gestures and detailed movements will make sure nothing is missed – we really need to see the flare gun 'fire' into the cable car rather than at Bradley. Smoke can be created via a hand-held smoke machine operated by a neutral performer. Bradley's jump should be slow motion and actually created by his being moved by the neutral actors. They deliver him safely to the other cable car made from stage blocks. Sudden blackness and then projected film of a ball of flame exploding outwards with a huge bang. As this dies to the sound of crackling flame, the only light is on Bradley as he delivers his 'Wow!' Blackout.

Act Two, Scene 10 (pp 90–102): Hospital

Heartbeat, very fast. Projected caption: 'Days later', which merges to a large 'hospital' red cross.

The neutral actors pick up Bradley from the stage blocks, transport him to the hospital bed and sit him up. The drip, neck-collar and leg-plaster can be quickly and easily placed. Using a couple of other blocks for visitors to sit on will help use the space.

The heartbeat slows as the scene starts, then fades in volume. The scene plays out naturalistically until the blackout.

Curtain

As the cast bow and the audience leave, consider using music which in some way refers to the plot ('Livin' On The Edge', 'Blaze Of Glory', 'Weapon of Choice', 'Ice Ice Baby') – even if it might be ironic and may raise a smile.

The fast-paced and diverse settings in *Ski Jump* can be staged well with a little hard work, imagination, ensemble playing and charm. My overall advice is to not let the staging get in the way of the acting. Keep it simple and always give clues to where we are. Never be afraid of making it obvious; audiences are used to film and television using 'signage-shots' to show where the scene is set (school, hospital, office) so don't be afraid to do the same. The words, the acting, the expressions and the gestures are the core of articulating this play. Make sure they stay to the fore.

I hope you find these suggestions useful. They are intended to give your cast as much responsibility as possible. They aim to give your pupils a sense of the kind of ensemble theatre-making which is widely used by companies like Complicité, Kneehigh and Improbable and will develop their performance skills rather than relying on expensive trickery.

Richard Conlon

Prologue

Hospital intensive care unit.

A doctor enters from behind a screen where a patient is having an emergency blood transfusion.

DOCTOR Have you informed the next of kin?

MEDIC 1 *(entering notes on a laptop)* They're on their way, doctor.

DOCTOR What did you tell them?

MEDIC 1 The basic facts. They know it's serious.   5
I spared them all the details.

DOCTOR Do they realise they might get here too late?
I can't be certain he'll respond to treatment.
The level of respiratory failure isn't looking
good at the moment.   10

MEDIC 1 I did warn them. I said the next twelve hours
are critical. I told them he's not yet stabilised,
that there are complications and we're doing
all we can.

DOCTOR He'll still need more blood if there's internal   15
bleeding. If he makes it to the morning, I'll run
another full scan to be on the safe side. Keep
monitoring his breathing.

MEDIC 1 And in the meantime?

DOCTOR We can only wait … and hope for the best.   20

MEDIC 2 *(coming out urgently from behind the screen)*
You're needed – quickly.

> *They rush back behind the screen.*

> *Blackout.*

ACT ONE   Scene One

Parents' evening in a school hall, months earlier.

Teachers sit behind desks, while pupils and their parents sit waiting in the middle of the room. Bradley and his dad are clearly stressed.

DAD *(very frustrated)* Attitude. That's your problem. In a nutshell – attitude.

BRADLEY *(bored)* Yeah, yeah, yeah.

DAD *(snapping)* Don't you 'yeah, yeah, yeah' me. *(lowering his voice as people stare)* Here rests   5
my case. You're jam-packed full of festering, repulsive, stinking attitude.

BRADLEY *(smirking)* No, Dad – that's the school drains. I hate parents' evening.

DAD Hardly surprising. This is the worst one yet.   10
All down to your attitude. Everyone can see it apart from you. It's oozing from every pore.

BRADLEY *(sighs)* No, that's acne. But I've got some good face scrub now.

DAD It's not a joking matter, Brad. When I was your   15
age I was much more focused. I can't think what's got into you. Can you imagine how embarrassing this is?

BRADLEY Yeah. I've never felt so embarrassed.

DAD Well, at least that's something. 20

BRADLEY I'm embarrassed by your shirt and socks.
They're gross.

DAD *(angrily)* Far too cheeky for your own good.
They all say it too. Every teacher tonight has
said the same. Your attitude lets you down. 25
I only pray our last appointment will bring us
a ray of hope.

BRADLEY *(shrugging)* Miss Farmer won't help. She's my
form teacher. She hates me. Can I go home?

DAD No. It's time you faced up to the truth. You 30
need to pull your socks up.

BRADLEY *(mumbling)* Not if they're like yours. *(he looks up
to see Katie across the room and waves)* Hi!

DAD Are you listening to me? You're more
concerned about your friends than getting 35
good grades. More interested in looking cool
in front of your mates.

MR MINHAS *(striding past)* Hi, Bradley – how's it going?

BRADLEY Don't ask, sir. Not good.

MR MINHAS This must be your father. Hello, Mr Stradling. 40
(shaking his hand) I have the pleasure of
taking Brad for trampoline in Gym Club. He's
a natural. I think Brad will go a long way with
his gymnastics. He's got just the right attitude.
Good to see you – sorry, must go. 45

Mr Minhas exits.

4

BRADLEY *(smiling for the first time)* At least somebody loves me.

DAD What use is trampolining to the world? It won't get you a job, will it?

BRADLEY It might. At a night club, maybe. 50

DAD Eh?

BRADLEY As a bouncer.

DAD *(tuts)* I wish you'd take things more seriously. This is your future we're talking about. My only child is about to end up on the scrap 55 heap. You don't know how depressing this is. I flew down especially for this – to show I care. I should have let your mother bring you and go through the humiliation of being told her son is an idle toad. What will she say about 60 all this?

BRADLEY *(suddenly reacting angrily)* She won't know! I won't tell her and I know you won't. Maybe if I had parents who spoke to each other and didn't live at opposite ends of the country, 65 I'd become the son you always dreamed of – with a squeaky-clean *(shouting)* ATTITUDE.

DAD Shhh, keep your voice down.

BRADLEY And don't lie to me, Dad. You didn't fly down especially for me at all. You'll be staying with 70 that woman from Head Office and claiming the trip on expenses.

DAD *(clearly guilty as charged)* If I'd spoken to my father like that at 14, I'd have got my head knocked off. Your mother's been far too soft on you. Discipline, that's what you need. They all say it. Cheeky and too lively. That's your problem. 75

BRADLEY Too lively? Would they rather have a classroom full of corpses? My teachers don't like me. It's not my fault if I find their lessons boring and it shows in my glazed eyes. Does it make me such a bad person if I'd rather be out with my mates than sitting like a zombie, being suffocated by the Corn Laws of 1802? 80 85

DAD *(smugly)* Fifteen.

BRADLEY What?

DAD Fifteen. The first Corn Law was 1815. And don't say it.

BRADLEY What? Don't say what? 90

DAD Don't look at me like I'm a complete nerd and say '*whatever*'. Just like you always do.

BRADLEY *(teasing, as his dad glares)* What … ever gives you that idea?

MISS FARMER *(standing at a desk, calling over)* Mr Stradling, sorry I'm running a few minutes late. Do come and take a seat. And you, Bradley. 95

BRADLEY *(whispering)* Here we go. Time for another trial by torture. Like a lamb to the slaughter. Execution by nagging — 100

DAD *(glaring)* Shhh.

MISS FARMER How's the evening going so far, Mr Stradling?

BRADLEY He's getting stressy, miss.

They sit at her desk.

MISS FARMER I didn't ask you, Bradley. I hope it hasn't been too uncomfortable, Mr Stradling. Knowing 105
Bradley as I do, I can imagine there have been some difficult issues.

DAD I think you've got the measure of my son, Miss Farmer. Tonight hasn't been easy.

MISS FARMER Then we have ten minutes to make a 110
difference. How about it, Bradley? Is it possible to go home on a positive note? What do you think you need to make things better?

BRADLEY A good psychiatrist?

DAD I don't think psychiatric help is quite what you 115
need.

BRADLEY I didn't mean me. I meant for you.

DAD *(thumping the table)* Will you take this more seriously? Sorry, Miss Farmer.

MISS FARMER I don't think we're getting off to a good start. 120
Let's take a different approach. I wonder if we can think how best to give Bradley's attitude a kick-start. Maybe we ought to consider incentives and alternatives. Carrots and sticks.

DAD Now you're talking. We had the stick when I 125
was at school and it didn't do me any harm.
Bring back the cane is what I say.

MISS FARMER I think we've moved on from those days, Mr Stradling. By 'carrot', I had one of my trips in mind. I organise a number of extracurricular 130 activities. The vacancies fill quickly but maybe Bradley might wish to consider skiing in Austria or joining my famous EuroDisney weekend. But, of course, he'd need to pull his socks up before his name went on the list. 135 What do you think?

BRADLEY I'm not sure if skiing is my thing.

MISS FARMER Really? Then you might be interested to learn that Katie's mother has just paid Katie's deposit for the trip. Katie said she was hoping 140 you'd be able to go too. Will that change your mind? This year's prices are very reasonable, Mr Stradling.

BRADLEY Where's your cheque book, Dad?

DAD After the way you've spoken to me tonight? 145

MISS FARMER I think we're going to need a few promises from you first, young man. No improvement in your attitude – no trip.

Miss Farmer reaches into her bag.

MISS FARMER Perhaps it would be a good time to hand this watch back to you, Mr Stradling. I had to 150 confiscate it in the middle of an important assembly. The alarm of a crowing cockerel is most inappropriate, I'm sure you agree. Bradley was given a severe warning and I don't want to see the watch in school again. 155

BRADLEY I didn't mean it to go off, honest. It was a mistake.

MISS FARMER It wasn't a mistake when you thumped a Year 8 boy for laughing at you at break. I don't know if you heard, Mr Stradling, but Bradley   160 received a temporary exclusion as a result of his outburst. Such violent behaviour isn't tolerated here.

BRADLEY *(angrily)* I was only standing up for myself!

MISS FARMER That's no excuse. Swearing at the supervisor   165 who reported you didn't help either.

DAD *(sighing)* I do apologise, Miss Farmer. Brad hasn't told me about this. I quite agree. There's absolutely no excuse for violence and I'm ashamed. He seems to lack all self-control.   170 I can't think what's wrong with him. *(pausing awkwardly, unable to look up)* And as for that watch, it won't happen again … will it, Brad?

BRADLEY No, it won't.

Bradley shuffles uncomfortably, then brightens.

BRADLEY So will I be able to go skiing?   175

DAD *(glaring)* That remains to be seen. I think we need to talk about a few things first.

MISS FARMER About what is appropriate, Bradley, and what is not. Your mission is to understand the difference. You might be bright but you're not   180 always wise.

DAD I'll do all I can to help, Miss Farmer, even

9

though my hands are tied somewhat, as I live some way away, in Glasgow. Miracles can happen but if I actually manage to do anything significant to improve my son's attitude, I'll eat my hat. 185

BRADLEY Make it your naff shirt and it's a deal.

MISS FARMER Not appropriate, Bradley.

BRADLEY *(laughing)* Hey listen, this is a good one … if you eat your baseball cap, Dad, it won't be my attitude – but your 'hat-he-chewed'. Get it? AT-TI-TUDE. 190

DAD *(shaking his head despairingly)* No, Brad. Not funny. 195

MISS FARMER Highly inappropriate. But already we've got a target in sight, Mr Stradling. Bradley is going to change for the better, you mark my words. I now see him as my own personal challenge. Leave it with me. We're in for a major epiphany with this young man. I feel it in my bones. 200

Miss Farmer stands to shake their hands. Bradley is speechless for once.

MISS FARMER Anything to add?

BRADLEY See you on the slopes, miss.

He and his dad walk away.

DAD That was even worse than I expected. 205

BRADLEY Can we just go? I'm dying for a takeaway.

DAD   *(raising his voice)* Just listen to me for once, will
        you? Don't you get it? You can't see what an
        absolute fool you're making of yourself – and
        making me look like a prize idiot!   210

BRADLEY   *(mumbling)* You seem pretty good at doing
           that for yourself.

DAD   *(shouting, everyone staring)* Don't you dare talk
        to me like that!

BRADLEY   *(really embarrassed)* Shhh, Dad, you're losing it.   215

DAD   I don't need any lectures from you about
        losing it. You're the one with the short fuse.
        Do you realise that getting excluded for
        violence has gone on your record? It's an
        appalling way to behave and I've never felt   220
        so ashamed of you! Where does this dreadful
        attitude come from?

BRADLEY   It must be in my genes. I blame the parents!

DAD   *(snapping angrily)* Well, it's not from me.
        I always knew your mother had something   225
        wrong with her and it's obvious to me —

BRADLEY   *(butting in)* Don't blame Mum. Why do you
           always blame everyone else? It's never your
           fault for anything, is it? And as for all that
           rubbish about the cane you were going on   230
           about – I mean, how embarrassing was that?
           (now getting really upset) You've never once
           told me I've done well at anything and you
           don't take any interest in my gym stuff. I'm fed

up with it and with no one EVER listening to 235
my side of things!

Bradley storms off.

BRADLEY *(shouting back)* And don't bother wagging
your finger at me and telling me I don't
deserve the ski trip because of my *(mockingly)*
'atrocious attitude'! 240

Bradley exits.

DAD *(shouting after him)* You are dead right! You
don't even deserve that takeaway!

*He looks round to see the whole room in silence
and everyone staring at him.*

DAD *(mumbling)* And you lot gawping like goldfish
doesn't make this any easier either.

Blackout.

Scene Two

Break time at school a few days later.

Bradley stands with an envelope in his mouth, trying to push a bag into his locker.

BRADLEY *(muffled)* Katie, come here a minute.

KATIE I didn't get a word of that. Take that out of your mouth so I can hear you.

BRADLEY It's a letter from my dad. It came this morning.

ADIOLA We talk to each other in our house. It saves a lot on stamps. 5

BRADLEY *(mockingly)* Duh! My dad lives in Glasgow – remember?

HARJIT So why doesn't he email or text? Is he that ancient? Did he write the letter with an old feather pen thing like that Charles Dickens guy? 10

BRADLEY I haven't opened this yet. I wanted to share the special moment with Katie.

KATIE You what, Brad? 15

BRADLEY My dad only posts something to me if it's you-know-what!

HARJIT Dosh! Is it a cheque or something?

BRADLEY I think so. This could be it. The moment I've been waiting for. I so hope I persuaded him 20 with all my 'I'm so sorry, Dad' after parents' evening.

HARJIT You'll look a right muppet if it's just a boring letter about the weather.

KATIE Go on, then. Open it. I bet it's not for the whole lot. 25

ADIOLA Oh, I see what you mean now. This could be the deposit for the ski trip.

HARJIT Miss Farmer said there's only a couple places left so you'd better be quick. 30

BRADLEY In that case … here goes … *(ripping open the envelope)* yeeeees! It's for the whole lot. The full whack! *(kissing the cheque)*

HARJIT *(trying to sound posh)* How terribly spiffing to have such a rich father. 35

KATIE *(hugging Bradley)* Brad, that's fantastic! We'll have such a great time in Austria. I'm so glad you're coming. You'll make it brilliant.

HARJIT Thanks a lot. I'm going too, remember.

ADIOLA And me. I paid my deposit ages ago. My mum's loaded. 40

BRADLEY Yeah, well now my dad's coughed up, you've all got me to worry about when I'm let loose on skis. I'll chase you down a few mountains and show you lot how to do it. Yeah! 45

They all high five.

Scene Three

On the dry-ski slope a few weeks later.

Everyone is shuffling awkwardly on skis, trying to stay upright. Only Miss Farmer is in control.

MISS FARMER Right, I want the starter group to stay here. Just shuffle yourselves to the side and Mr Minhas will come and talk you through how to do a snowplough turn. I'll join you shortly once I've sorted out the others. 5

> *Miss Farmer exits.*
> *The students are all very wobbly on their skis, standing in a row and clinging to their ski poles.*

KATIE I can't move in these things. How are you supposed to get anywhere? *(falling)* Aaah!

BRADLEY I feel like a pregnant penguin waddling over a giant toothbrush.

ADIOLA You certainly look like one, Brad. *(falling)* Aaah! 10

BRADLEY At least I don't look like a *dead* pregnant penguin!

HARJIT Here comes Mr Cool. How come AJ is so good? Just look at him move.

AJ *(sweeping on with style)* Evening all! How's it 15 going? Looks like we're still finding our feet, I see.

BRADLEY	I've lost mine forever. AJ, how come you're so good?
AJ	I've been coming here since Year 7. I'm one of Miss Farmer's stars. Don't worry, once you get on real snow it'll be a piece of cake.
ADIOLA	You reckon?
AJ	Definitely in your case, Adiola. Angel-cake! See yer. I'm off to the top for another AJ spectacular.

AJ exits.

HARJIT	Yo, Ad – looks like he fancies you, Miss Angel-Cake!
ADIOLA	I can live with that. He's cool.
KATIE	Then you'd better get up on your feet for when he comes back. You don't look at your best like that. *(falling again)* Aaah!

Everyone laughs as Mr Minhas enters.

MR MINHAS	It's good you all see the funny side, folks. What we need to do is get those leg muscles working. So just space yourselves out a bit and we'll do some warm-ups.
BRADLEY	It might take a while, sir. Our legs are a bit like lumps of mush at the minute.
MR MINHAS	I'd have thought you'd be like Superman, Brad – what with your gym training.
HARJIT	Not quite, sir. More like Penguin Man.

Sound of a cockerel crowing – Bradley's watch alarm.

BRADLEY *(switching it off)* Oops, sorry about that. Mustn't let Miss Farmer hear it.

MR MINHAS You're right, Brad. Best keep that well out of sight and earshot if you value your life. 45

KATIE How long have you been able to ski, sir?

MR MINHAS Not long, Katie. It's amazing what you can achieve with a bit of adrenaline and total panic. Now then, all of you … straighten your legs and space yourselves out … 50

The pupil on the end falls and they all go down like dominoes, landing in a heap and giggling helplessly – just as Miss Farmer comes back, clearly not amused.

MISS FARMER *(shouting)* Just stop all this nonsense immediately! This is a public place and you're all acting like three-year-olds. And yes, I did hear that ridiculous watch of yours, Bradley Stradling. You know my views on that matter 55 and I shall be having words with you about that as soon as all of you take this lesson seriously and get up on your feet. Mr Minhas, could you go up to the advanced group and give them some practice on parallel turns? 60

MR MINHAS Sure.

Mr Minhas goes, looking somewhat embarrassed.

BRADLEY	Sorry, miss. It was my fault.
MISS FARMER	I'm fully aware of that. No one else would be so immature.
KATIE	Will we ever get to ski like you, miss? You make it look so easy.

65

MISS FARMER	You have to work at it – like any skill.
ADIOLA	Did you start when you were really little, Miss Farmer?
MISS FARMER	Yes, I did. It's quite handy having a father who is half Swiss.

70

BRADLEY	Which half? Top or bottom? That could make a difference.

Everyone laughs, Miss Farmer glares.

HARJIT	So did you learn to ski when you were a toddler, miss?

75

MISS FARMER	Of course. I was practically born wearing skis.
BRADLEY	Ouch! Your poor mum. Just imagine popping out with those things on.
MISS FARMER	Bradley, that is quite enough and most inappropriate. I'm getting very tired of your childish humour. And as always, I'm irritated by your unfortunate attitude. In fact, I blame you for spoiling this group. I shall be having words with your father. It's not too late to have you removed from my Austria ski trip, you know.

80

85

BRADLEY	But I was only —

18

KATIE *(butting in)* He's lovely really, miss. Tell you what, Brad and I will come here at the weekend and practise like mad. Then we'll show you what we can do. 90

BRADLEY Yeah, we'll make you dead proud. Except I can't do this weekend, Katie. I've got to fly up to see my dad. I'm off to Glasgow on Friday.

MISS FARMER Then all I can say, Bradley, is that I hope your 95 poor father is able to drum a bit of sense into you and get that attitude of yours under control once and for all.

Scene Four

On board a plane to Glasgow.

Mandy brings Bradley onto the plane before the other passengers. The rows of seats are empty but they soon fill up.

MANDY *(showing Bradley to his seat)* Here we go – this is your seat, Brad. By the window just over the wing.

BRADLEY Great – thanks.

Bradley squeezes in and sits, peering out of the window.

MANDY Let me pop your bag up in the locker for you. 5
Then you can make yourself nice and comfy as the other passengers come aboard. Have you flown as an unaccompanied minor before?

BRADLEY Yeah – loads of times. Mum and Dad are always sending me from one to the other. 10
They never speak to each other so I'm always travelling by myself. I don't mind.

MANDY Don't you worry, love – I'll be keeping my eye on you. When I bring round the snacks, I'll see what I can find especially for you. And when 15
we land at Glasgow, you just stay put while everyone gets off and then I'll take you to

20

meet your dad in arrivals. How's that? You're my special VIP.

BRADLEY Cool. That's if Dad remembers. He's always late. 20

MANDY Not to worry, we'll sort you out. Just don't be like my last stroppy teenager. She was a nightmare.

BRADLEY Bit of an attitude problem, was it?

MANDY Big time. What a little madam. What a big attitude. 25

BRADLEY Hmmm. I know the feeling.

Lipstud is waiting to get to his seat.

MANDY Oops! Sorry, sir. Is this your seat? I'll get out of the way. I'll come and see you in a bit, Brad. OK?

Lipstud puts his bag up in the locker.

LIPSTUD I hope this flight will be on time.

MANDY As far as I know there are no hold-ups, sir. 30

Mandy goes and Lipstud sits next to Bradley.

BRADLEY This flight isn't often late. I've done this one loads of times. There's only a problem if someone's luggage goes missing. They're pretty tight on security and stuff.

LIPSTUD *(giving Brad a long stare)* Is that so? 35

BRADLEY There's sometimes a bit of a delay when we get to Glasgow. They've had a few security scares at the airport. Dad was there a few years back when a terrorist set off a firebomb, so ever since they often search hand luggage with 40 sniffer dogs when you get on or off the plane.

21

LIPSTUD *(sarcastically)* Most reassuring.

BRADLEY Not that it affects me. One of the good things about being an unaccompanied minor is that the stewardess takes me straight through any 45 queues. I guess they can tell I'm not likely to blow the place up.

LIPSTUD *(thoughtfully)* Right. Worth knowing.

BRADLEY Not that I could hide much of a bomb in my hand luggage or inside my boxer shorts. 50

LIPSTUD You'd be surprised.

BRADLEY *(looking to the front)* She's giving us the safety talk – what to do in the event of a water landing. They make it sound like a pleasant splash in the ocean. We just pop on 55 a life-jacket, blow a whistle and wait to be rescued. They don't mention g-force, massive disintegration and instant annihilation.

LIPSTUD *(abruptly)* Maybe just listen and pay attention to what she says. 60

Lipstud stands to reach into the locker and opens his bag. Eventually he sits, with a magazine.

BRADLEY Sorry. I always gabble a lot before take-off. Must be the excitement. I love it when we speed down the runway, don't you?

LIPSTUD *(becoming irritated)* No.

BRADLEY Sorry. Oh, here we go. Listen to those engines 65 revving. Prepare for take-off, captain …

Blackout.

Scene Five

Glasgow Airport – the arrivals area.

BRADLEY *(sitting on his own, talking into his mobile)*
Where are you, Dad? Yeah, I've been sitting
here waiting for you for ten minutes. Yeah,
the flight was fine. The stewardess left me
for a bit. There are loads of queues again for
bag checks and stuff. Luckily I walked right 5
through. Security guys all over the place.
They must be on the look-out for something
scary – so don't arrive in a stupid shirt.

    Pause.

BRADLEY How long? Another what? Half hour! Don't
tell me it's traffic again. Why the roadblocks? 10
Well, if security is extra tight round the airport
tonight you'd better get a move on and rescue
your only son. OK then, Dad. See you soon.

    Lipstud appears beside him.

LIPSTUD Hi. Still on your own?

BRADLEY Yeah. My dad's held up in traffic. Security 15
police. He reckons they're expecting trouble
somewhere. He says it's probably me!

LIPSTUD You want a Coke? Coffee? Want to join me in
Starbucks?

23

BRADLEY I wouldn't mind some crisps. I'm starving.   20

LIPSTUD OK, be my guest.

BRADLEY *(following Lipstud into Starbucks)* With a bit of
luck Dad will get me a burger on the way to
Gran's. I haven't eaten all day apart from on
the plane.   25

LIPSTUD OK. You sit there and keep the table for us. I'll
get some food. Put my bag on the chair and
guard it with your life.

Lipstud exits.

BRADLEY Cheers.

Mandy appears.

MANDY Ah, there you are, Brad. I just wanted to check   30
you're OK. It looks like your dad turned up at
last, I see.

BRADLEY Well actually, he's not —

MANDY Look, I can't stay. It's a tight turnaround and
they'll be boarding for the flight back. Nice to   35
have met you. Bye.

Mandy exits.

BRADLEY So much for customer care.

He takes out his mobile to text Katie.

BRADLEY *(texting)* Hi Katie. Now in Glasgow. Will speak
2mro. CYL. Brad.

*Lipstud returns with a tray and sits opposite
Bradley.*

24

LIPSTUD I've got you some crisps. I see what you mean 40
about those queues at security. They searched
through everything in my bag. I saw you walk
right past.

BRADLEY Yeah – do you want a crisp?

LIPSTUD No. Listen to me. I'll get to the point. How 45
would you like to earn big money?

BRADLEY *(looking up mid-crisp)* Eh?

LIPSTUD For doing nothing. Just for what you've done
now. I'll give you one grand.

BRADLEY *(frowning)* I don't know what you mean. 50

LIPSTUD Open your bag.

BRADLEY What?

LIPSTUD Go on. Just open your bag. Now.

BRADLEY What for?

> *Bradley unzips his bag and looks inside. He
> takes out a book.*

BRADLEY What's this? 55

LIPSTUD Thank you. *(taking the book)* You see – one
thousand pounds for knowing nothing.
Simple.

BRADLEY When did you put that book in my bag?

LIPSTUD On the plane. You brought it through security 60
for me and didn't know.

BRADLEY But it's only a book. I mean … hold on, it's
not just a book, is it? It's hollowed out. There's
something inside it.

25

LIPSTUD That needn't bother you. Do you want a 65
grand? Cash. I'll give you half now.

BRADLEY *(very puzzled)* So what are you asking me to
do exactly?

LIPSTUD Just let me know when you're doing that
journey again. That's all there is to it. 70

BRADLEY Are you … some sort of dealer? Is it drugs or
something?

LIPSTUD *(thumping the table)* Do I really seem like some
drugged-up crack cowboy? Let's just say I'm
on a mission and I intend to leave my mark 75
right here. So just say 'yes' or 'no'. 'Yes' and you
get five hundred pounds now. 'No' and that's
the end of it. Take it or leave it.

BRADLEY *(pausing while munching a crisp)* What if I get
caught? What if I tell the police? 80

LIPSTUD *(leaning forward and whispering threateningly)*
Then I'll kill you. Those who are not with
us are against us. The enemy. They will be
eradicated.

BRADLEY Are you a student or something? One of those
hotheads my dad talks about? 85

LIPSTUD I am an activist. A student of revolution. And
you can be part of it. Yes or no?

BRADLEY *(fidgeting uncomfortably)* This is kind of weird.
You seem a bit random.

LIPSTUD That's OK by me. So – will you do a deal? 90

BRADLEY Let me put it this way. My mum's always going on about 'stranger danger' …

LIPSTUD *(becoming increasingly impatient)* And your point is?

BRADLEY This deal has too many questions. And for that 95 reason you can count me out.

LIPSTUD *(standing)* I thought for a minute you were a bright kid. But you're like all the others. Your attitude, like everyone's, is going to change. Big time. 100

    Lipstud exits.

BRADLEY *(shaking his head)* Yeah, yeah, whatever. Thanks for the crisps though.

    He stares ahead, with a frown.

Scene Six

Glasgow Airport – the enquiries desk.

A frazzled member of staff is busy working at a computer.

BRADLEY Excuse me, I need to report something.

STAFF Just wait, lad. I'll be with you in a jiffy.

BRADLEY The thing is, I've met a weirdo who wanted me to —

STAFF Hold on. *(squinting at the computer screen)*   5
No, that can't be right. It's got to be
Amsterdam.

BRADLEY *(leaning forward and whispering secretively)*
The guy next to me on the plane. He offered
me money to carry stuff.

> *The member of staff is still absorbed in what's
> on the screen.*

STAFF According to this it's 20.16 to Addis Ababa.   10

BRADLEY *(knocking on the desk)* Hello? Is anybody in
there?

STAFF *(clearly angered)* I told you to wait.

BRADLEY OK then. Shall we just stand here while he
breaks a few more security rules?   15

STAFF Listen, pal … what's your problem? Jokes
about security are not welcome here.

BRADLEY The guy next to me on the plane – he was like a student but a bit of a psycho. Well, he hid something in my bag and I brought it through the bag checks because I'm an unaccompanied minor. 20

STAFF Ah, a PIN, eh? I might have known.

BRADLEY Sorry?

STAFF *(shuffling through papers, without looking up)* Just my shorthand for unaccompanied minors. Kids on their own I call PIN. Pain In the Neck. They're often trouble. 25

BRADLEY Well, I'm not trouble – I'm trying to warn you about this guy. I think he could even be some sort of terrorist. He said he'd pay me a thousand pounds to bring stuff through in my bag. He put his book in here without me knowing. 30

Bradley shows his bag.

STAFF Let me look. *(opening the bag and looking inside)* There doesn't appear to be anything suspicious, apart from your taste in DVDs. 35

BRADLEY No, there's nothing in there now because he took it back.

STAFF Who? What's this person's name?

BRADLEY No idea. He didn't tell me. 40

STAFF What's he look like?

BRADLEY Just an average, student-looking guy. Taller than me. Jeans, dark sweatshirt … er …

leather jacket. Smart trainers. Stubbly chin
and a stud thing in his bottom lip. Scary eyes.   45

STAFF Sounds like half the guys in Glasgow. What do
you expect me to do? Did he assault you or
something? Is this an official complaint?
If so, you'll need to fill in a form.

BRADLEY I'm not complaining, I'm warning. There's   50
a guy round here who's carrying stuff. I've
got no idea what it is but I could tell he's
got something planned, something bad.
He wanted me to help him. He's got a
book, the one he hid in my bag, and it's got   55
something inside.

STAFF Yeah, most books do. They're called words.
Listen, son, I saw the sort of DVD you've
got in your bag. Quite a bit of fantasy and
spy stuff. It looks like you've just got a bit   60
of an extreme imagination. If this guy exists,
where is he exactly?

BRADLEY How do I know? Look at this place, it's full
of people. He walked off. He could be
anywhere by now. I realise you think I'm   65
just a stupid teenager. If I was a bit older, you'd
have to take me seriously, wouldn't you? Well,
I'm getting fed up with everyone thinking I'm
just a stroppy kid, do you hear? *(banging the
desk)* No one ever listens to me!   70

STAFF *(clearly annoyed)* Cool it, lad. You might like to
know I'm about to alert security to the fact

that I'm being hassled by an over-excitable boy with an implausible story and no evidence whatsoever. Within seconds of me pressing the button, you will be frogmarched from the building and you won't be allowed to travel to or from here as an unaccompanied minor again. So it's up to you, pal. Either you go away quietly and forget this nonsense or you risk a great deal of unpleasant attention, public humiliation and possible arrest. The choice is entirely yours.   75   80

BRADLEY   This is mad. Do you treat everyone like this?

STAFF   Only those who waste my time, pal. So go   85
and find someone else to annoy. In fact, I'll escort you to the door myself; it's quicker. This way, son.

BRADLEY   *(being led away)* Hey, there he is. That's the guy over there. The one on the plane.   90

STAFF   Enough, lad, shut up. I've heard enough.

BRADLEY   I can't believe you're so stupid. Why won't you listen to me? And it's me who's supposed to be the one with an attitude problem.

STAFF   *(pushing Bradley out through the door)* On   95
your way, son. And don't hurry back.

BRADLEY   Don't blame me if you get blown up, you idiot!

Bradley turns and comes face to face with his dad.

31

DAD   Whatever's going on? What's the problem?

BRADLEY   They won't believe me, Dad.   100

STAFF   Just take him home, sir. Your lad's got one big attitude problem.

DAD   *(in despair)* Oh great, Bradley, you've done it again. That's all I need. Just the way to start a terrific father–son bonding weekend.   105 Why don't you ever learn?

Blackout.

Scene Seven

The school changing rooms a week later.

Mr Minhas is addressing the gymnastics team (including Bradley, Harjit and AJ).

MR MINHAS *(consulting his clipboard)* So that's the last Gym Club for a while, as some of us will be away next week on the Austria trip. Many of you are doing really well and it's time to think about proficiency awards. AJ and Harjit, it's time to   5
think about your Silver on vault and rebound.

AJ No sweat!

MR MINHAS You just need to polish up Number 6: *From a short run along a bench, rebound from trampette and tuck jump to land softly*. Keep   10
watching Brad's technique. You're ready for Gold, Brad. You just need to polish up your straddle jump.

BRADLEY Cool! But what about trampoline, sir?

MR MINHAS I was coming to that. Harjit is ready for Award   15
11 on trampoline gymnastics. You just need to tighten up those backward somersaults, Harjit.

HARJIT I'm working on it, sir. Don't worry, I'll keep watching the master. OK, Brad?   20

33

BRADLEY There'll just be a small charge.

MR MINHAS I have to say, Brad … despite all your troubles of late, you've been focusing really well. I think you're ready for Award 12. You did some great crash dives just then.   25

BRADLEY My life is one massive crash dive right now, sir.

MR MINHAS Yeah, I wanted to have a little chat with you, actually. OK everyone, gather up your kit and we'll talk about competitions next   30 time. Keep looking at the notice board. See you soon.

AJ AND HARJIT Cheers, sir. See you, Brad.

AJ and Harjit exit.

BRADLEY *(tying his laces)* So you've heard about my disastrous weekend have you, sir?   35

MR MINHAS I gather your dad and Miss Farmer have been in discussion. It seems your place on the ski trip is now in question. Your dad thinks you shouldn't go after all.

BRADLEY I can't seem to do anything right. I got   40 thrown out of the airport for making a fuss. I know I was a bit irritated and probably really annoying but I had to report this scary nutcase from the plane. I just get fed up with being treated like a little kid.   45

MR MINHAS You're not the only one, Brad. So how did your dad deal with it?

BRADLEY   With a massive outburst in the car park.
He marched me back into the airport to
apologise. I had to grovel and say, 'Sorry I   50
over-reacted in such a childish way.' But the
fact is, sir, the guy on the plane offered to
pay me to carry something for him. I really
didn't imagine it all, despite what they say.
I thought what he asked me to do was well   55
out of order so I felt I had to report it. People
never believe me.

MR MINHAS   I'd have done the same, Brad. Maybe you
just chose the wrong person to tell or the
wrong way to do it. It happens. I'm sure you've   60
learned a lot from this.

BRADLEY   Yeah – I've learned I can't trust anyone. And
I've learned that my dad doesn't think much
of me.

MR MINHAS   Give him time and he will. How would you feel   65
if I phoned him?

BRADLEY   If you want. It won't do any good.

MR MINHAS   It might help you get back on the ski trip.

BRADLEY   I doubt it. Besides, even if I do go, Miss Farmer
will be breathing down my neck all the time.   70
If I put a foot wrong, she'll be on the phone to
Dad again. No one ever sees my side of things.
No one ever thinks I'm any good.

MR MINHAS   Brad, I've just been singing your praises for
the last hour! I can see a lot of good in you   75
and I don't just mean in the gym. Just because

you've got a short fuse doesn't make you a bad person. Let's just say you've got spirit.

BRADLEY Mum blames hormones. She reckons all the world's problems are caused by hormones, 80 especially mine and my dad's. *(pausing thoughtfully)* Are you really going to phone my dad?

MR MINHAS Tell you what, Brad – give me a chance. I'll see what I can do. And listen to me … if it makes 85 you feel a bit better, I think you're a great lad. Seriously. And I want you to believe in yourself too. The ski trip could be the making of you.

BRADLEY Cheers, sir. But I'm pretty certain I'll be staying 90 at home while you're all skiing down the mountains and having a great time. Don't forget to send me a postcard.

Bradley exits, looking sorry for himself.

Scene Eight

On the ski coach (on the motorway).

The teachers are sitting at the front of the coach just behind the driver.

AJ, Harjit, Adiola and Katie are at the back, playing games on their mobile phones.

Bradley is with them, listening to music on his iPod.

MISS FARMER   *(calling back)* Bradley, could you come down to the front for a minute? I'd like a word.

> *Bradley doesn't hear her as his music is playing too loudly.*

MISS FARMER   *(louder)* BRADLEY!

> *Bradley looks surprised, turns off his iPod and starts to walk towards Miss Farmer.*

AJ   *(shouting from the back seat)* Don't sign anything, Brad!   5

MISS FARMER   Thank you, Alexander. We don't need your comments. Not appropriate.

BRADLEY   *(reaching the front)* Yes, miss? You wanted something?

MISS FARMER   Yes, sit down a minute. I didn't get a chance   10 to speak with you before we left. It was only at the last minute that Mr Minhas was able

37

to persuade us all to let you come. But now
you're here, I'm looking forward to being
impressed by your change in attitude. That   15
said, I had to organise the rooms before I
knew you'd be joining us. So I'm afraid you'll
be in a room on your own. Sorry, but you
won't be sharing a bedroom with your friends.
Solitary confinement at lights out, I'm afraid.   20

BRADLEY   That's OK, miss. I don't mind.

MISS FARMER   Good. In fact, you'll be the only one on the top
floor. The good news is you've got a balcony
with a lovely view of the mountains. The bad
news is my room is immediately under yours   25
so I'll hear what you're up to.

BRADLEY   In that case —

MISS FARMER   Don't say it, Bradley, whatever it was …
I can tell when you're about to be rude.
Remember, this week is your big opportunity   30
to make the right impression.

BRADLEY   Yes, miss. I won't let you down.

MISS FARMER   Good. Your father has asked to be kept
informed should there be any …

BRADLEY   There won't be, miss. I'll be an angel all week.   35
It might kill me but I'll do it.

MISS FARMER   Good. This week is your chance to prove
yourself once and for all. To be honest, you've
been the big question mark over this trip.
Even now I see you've got that silly watch.   40
And I heard your mobile alarm earlier too.

I don't want any cause for complaint from me or from anyone, do you understand?

BRADLEY I understand, Miss Farmer.

MISS FARMER Just as well. I had to fill in a risk assessment   45
for this trip and you're on it in big letters.
Make sure you keep your comments to
yourself, especially when the public are
around. The first test will be shortly, when we
get to Eurotunnel.   50

BRADLEY *(miming zipping his mouth)* My lips will be
sealed.

STEVE Just to say, Miss Farmer, there's a hold-up
ahead. There's a message to say the tunnel is
closed. A couple of hours' delay.   55

MISS FARMER That's all we need. You see, Bradley, I've got
enough on my plate already. Can we stop
somewhere, Steve?

STEVE I suggest we get as far as we can and wait at
the service area nearest the tunnel. The kids   60
can have a break and stretch their legs while I
find out what's going on.

BRADLEY You can use my phone to go online to the AA,
miss. That's what my dad does to get travel
information.   65

MISS FARMER Thank you for your advice, Bradley. If I need
your input, I'll let you know. Now, back you go
to join your friends.

Miss Farmer takes out her phone and calls.

STEVE They probably won't be able to tell you much. I expect a train has broken down. 70

MR MINHAS Let's hope things get put right quickly before the kids start getting too restless.

MISS FARMER *(switching off her phone)* Apparently the tunnel is swarming with police. They found what they call 'suspicious material' on the train. That's all 75 we need. What a pain.

BRADLEY And for once, miss, the pain isn't me!

Blackout.

Scene Nine

A motorway service station.

Bradley, Katie, Adiola, Harjit and AJ are sitting at a table covered in chocolate-bar wrappers.

ADIOLA *(looking at her watch)* This time tomorrow we'll be at the hotel in the mountains. I can't wait.

HARJIT Unless we're stuck here all night. Miss Farmer is well stressed at the thought of a bomb on the train. 5

KATIE To be honest, Harjit, I'm pretty worried myself.

AJ It's only a scare. They have them all the time.

KATIE According to Miss Farmer, the police found something they call 'explosive material'.

AJ Probably a box of matches or a cigarette 10 lighter.

ADIOLA Maybe someone was taking fireworks on holiday – as you do!

HARJIT There are some weirdos about, Ad. Talking of which, why are you so quiet, Brad? 15

BRADLEY I'm scared to say a word in case I offend 'she who must be obeyed'.

KATIE *(ruffling Bradley's hair)* I'm so glad they let you come at the last minute, Brad. It just wouldn't

be the same without you. You'll be a right   20
laugh up on the ski slopes.

ADIOLA If we ever get there.

AJ I'm getting some more chips. Anyone
interested?

HARJIT Yeah – we'll all share yours, AJ.   25

AJ It will be my pleasure. *(walking away and
knocking a drink over Bradley's legs)* Oops!
Sorry, Brad.

*Bradley remains perfectly still and puts on a
long-suffering voice.*

BRADLEY Never mind, AJ. I don't mind. Just tell Miss
Farmer that I haven't made the slightest fuss!   30

Everyone laughs.

BRADLEY I hope you're all impressed with my new
attitude – even though I'm soaked to my
boxers in Coke. *(standing)* I'll be back after a
scrub in the gents.

Bradley exits.

KATIE Poor Brad. Everyone's been nagging him   35
lately. He so needs cheering up.

ADIOLA Come on, Katie – you know what he's like.
He could drive anyone mad when he's in one
of his moods. I'm not surprised everyone's
been having a go at him.   40

HARJIT Yeah, but he doesn't mean to get on
teachers' nerves. Not all the time. You must

42

admit he's a good laugh. I agree with Katie, he's going to make this trip fun.

KATIE Yeah, it wouldn't be the same without Brad   45
keeping us on our toes with his tricks.

ADIOLA I can never tell when he's telling the truth or doing one of his stupid jokes.

Bradley rushes back and sits down, looking worried.

BRADLEY I'm not sure what to do.

ADIOLA Just get some paper towels. It's no big deal,   50
Brad.

BRADLEY No, I saw him. He was just going into the loo.
That bloke I met at the airport. The weird one.
What is he doing here? Unless … what if it's
him with a bomb?   55

HARJIT Whoa – just hold it, Brad. Get a grip. What are you on about?

KATIE You mean that student guy who offered you money? Are you sure it's him?

BRADLEY Certain. I'm absolutely certain. He didn't see   60
me. I've got to tell miss.

KATIE No. Don't do that, please.

BRADLEY But what if this guy really is a terrorist?

ADIOLA Don't go there, Brad. What if he isn't?

HARJIT Let it go, Brad. It's not worth making a fuss.   65
It's just a coincidence.

KATIE Harjit's right. It's best not to do anything, Brad.

BRADLEY But what if …? I remember his eyes. They were scary. I mean it. Seriously evil. He's dangerous. This could mean big trouble. 70

MISS FARMER *(arriving at the table)* Did I hear you use the word 'trouble', young Stradling? Surely not. Listen, we all need to get back on the coach. The crisis is over and the tunnel is open again so we should be off. Finish your drinks and be 75 back on board in no more than two minutes.

KATIE OK, miss.

Miss Farmer goes.

KATIE Come on then. Just forget it, Brad.

BRADLEY I can't. *(grabbing his phone)* If no one believes me, I'll get the evidence. I'll take a picture of 80 him and let the police decide.

Bradley runs off.

ADIOLA He's going to need telling. He can't go off on one of his crazy ideas now.

HARJIT Leave it with me. I'll stop him making a complete fool of himself. 85

Harjit goes after Bradley.

KATIE I just hope he isn't going to do something really stupid. That's the last thing we need right now.

Scene Ten

Another part of the service station, a minute later.

A young woman (Lipstud's girlfriend) with a scorpion tattoo on the back of her hand is sitting at a table overlooking the car park. She is listening to music on an iPod and tapping on the table.

Lipstud rushes over.

LIPSTUD Quick, get your things. We need to move.

GIRLFRIEND You must have left stuff on the train. Or the contact did. I've just heard it on the local news – they've searched the train and tunnel.

LIPSTUD What? Are you sure?   5

GIRLFRIEND Police dogs found traces. Maybe one of the boxes split. I told you —

LIPSTUD Not now. Not here. Get me a notepad, quick. That coach there, it's just pulling out.

Lipstud scribbles on the pad.

GIRLFRIEND What are you talking about?   10

LIPSTUD I've got the phone number off the side of the coach. It's a school trip and that kid is on it. The one I told you about at Glasgow Airport. I can't believe it. *(thumping the table)* How did he suddenly appear round here?   15

GIRLFRIEND Did he see you here?

LIPSTUD He took my photo and ran. I tried to catch him to get his phone but he got on that coach. He knows too much. I've got to stop him. I've got to do something or … 20

Lipstud takes out his mobile phone and taps in some numbers.

GIRLFRIEND Or what? Surely a kid isn't going to get in our way.

Lipstud speaks into his phone.

LIPSTUD Hi, is that Peargate Coaches? Right, one of your coaches with a school party has just left my service station and it's heading for 25 Eurotunnel. I'm the manager and one of the teachers left a credit card behind and I guess they'll need it. Can you let me know where they're going so I can send it to them? Yeah, I'll wait. *(to his girlfriend)* Get ready to change 30 all our plans.

GIRLFRIEND What? We're not going to catch him now, are we?

LIPSTUD *(clenching his fist and thumping the chair)* I've got to. I can't let him get away. That kid took me 35 by surprise. I should have grabbed him and broken his neck.

Lipstud speaks into his phone again.

LIPSTUD I've no idea what the name is on the card. One of my staff has it – I just noted the number on

your coach. If you don't want to tell me where   40
they're going, I'll just throw the card away
and you'll have to tell them your stupid rules
stopped me trying to help. No, I don't want to
hold on any more.

GIRLFRIEND *(stroking his arm)* Don't stress yourself. We'll   45
think of something.

LIPSTUD *(still on the phone)* Yes, I'll post it to the address.
That's what I said, didn't I?

GIRLFRIEND Keep your voice down. *(putting her arm round
him)* People are staring.   50

LIPSTUD Where? *(writing on a notepad)* Yes, I've got that.
(aside) That's just what I need.

Lipstud puts the phone away and grabs his bag.

LIPSTUD Come on, we've got a job to do.

GIRLFRIEND Where exactly?

LIPSTUD *(tapping details into a sat-nav)* We've got a long   55
journey. Austria. But I've got to get him.

GIRLFRIEND What?! You really think this kid is that much
of a threat?

LIPSTUD He's bright and he knows too much already.
I'm not going to let him upset things any   60
more. *(waving his fist)* He's going to pay
for this.

GIRLFRIEND Keep calm. You're working yourself up and
getting stressed. Take one of your tablets.

LIPSTUD Don't patronise me. I'm not an invalid.   65

GIRLFRIEND But you know very well you're due for your
next treatment. We shouldn't be heading
off to Austria with your transfusion date
next week.

LIPSTUD *(shouting)* I've dealt with this all my life! A few   70
extra days won't make any difference!

GIRLFRIEND OK, OK … calm down. We'll deal with this
together. Let's not do anything stupid.

LIPSTUD *(furious with her)* Stupid? Stupid? Don't you
dare accuse me of being stupid. You know   75
very well I will never be beaten. My plan
cannot and will not fail. I will do whatever it
takes for the cause. It's too important to be
derailed by a kid. It's a serious set-back but it
will give me great pleasure to get rid of this   80
particular irritation once and for all. I've made
up my mind – he must be eradicated.

They exit in a hurry.

Act Two   Scene One

Austria. First day of skiing. In a mountain café.

Bradley, Katie, AJ and Harjit are sitting at a table in their ski boots.

Bradley is looking thoughtfully at an image on his mobile phone.

KATIE I see what you mean, Brad. He looks well scary. His eyes look a bit wild.

AJ It's not a crime to look weird. If it was, Brad would've been locked up years ago.

ADIOLA *(arriving at the table)* Oh, you're not still looking   5
at that guy on your phone, are you? Just forget him, Brad.

BRADLEY But what if he's doing something bad right now and I could have stopped him?

HARJIT Come on, Brad. Even if this guy is a mad   10
axe murderer or another Jack the Ripper, there's nothing you can do about it. So put that phone away and enjoy the view from the window. Just look at the sun on the mountains. It's magic out there.   15

BRADLEY Yeah – I guess you're right. I need to forget it. I'll worry about 'Lipstud' when I get home.

I need to give all my mental energy to staying upright on skis.

KATIE I can never get off the ski lift without landing in a heap. It was dead embarrassing when I pulled Mr Minhas down as well. Did you see his face? 20

ADIOLA *(head in hands)* I just need sleep. We should never have spent all night gossiping. It was a right laugh, though. 25

AJ Yeah – while poor little Brad was all alone on the top floor.

HARJIT I hope Brad didn't look down from his balcony and get a glimpse of Miss Farmer in her nightie with a mug of cocoa. Now that would make a far scarier photo! 30

BRADLEY I was tempted to bash on the floor and shout down that she should keep the snoring under control but somehow I don't think she'd have seen the joke. 35

ADIOLA You could phone her. She gave us her number in case of emergency.

KATIE Can you imagine phoning her at two in the morning: 'please, miss, I can't get to sleep – stop that snoring.' 40

BRADLEY Hey, Katie – phone me right now, will you? You've got to hear the new ringtone I downloaded. It's meant to be gunshots from an M14 rifle. It's so cool. 45

AJ This I've got to hear!

They are unaware Miss Farmer has come in.

KATIE Right, here goes …

HARJIT Take cover, everyone.

Loud gunshots from Bradley's phone.
Miss Farmer frowns.

ADIOLA That's brilliant!

They all laugh but stop as Miss Farmer storms over.

MISS FARMER Just what do you think you're doing? That   50
stupid noise is so inappropriate and I told
you specifically, Bradley Stradling, not to
use any of your silly gimmicks on this trip.
Mobile phones are for emergency use only
and not for ridiculous noises like that. You can   55
hand over your phone to me right now and
I will consider returning it only when I feel
confident you can be trusted.

Bradley hands it to her.

BRADLEY But, miss, I didn't think —

MISS FARMER Exactly. You didn't think. That's exactly your   60
problem lately, you just don't think. And
don't you dare let me hear that watch of
yours.

Miss Farmer goes.

ADIOLA *(whispering)* I don't think she slept last night
either. I still think your ringtone's cool.   65

AJ Hey, look right up there to the top of that mountain. Can you see the cable car?

HARJIT You'd need a good head for heights up there. Look at the massive drop.

KATIE I bet even Brad would find that scary. 70

BRADLEY No problem. Heights never bother me. The only thing that scares me is bossy old bags like her. I've got Farmer-phobia. She's got it in for me big-time.

AJ Did you switch your phone off, Brad? 75

BRADLEY I didn't have time. She just snatched it … hey, are you giving me wicked ideas, AJ?

AJ Sort of. I might just happen to give it a call at three in the morning!

BRADLEY It'll certainly make her *shoot* out of bed! 80

They groan/laugh as Mr Minhas enters.

MR MINHAS Come on, you lot. All this hilarity must mean you're up to mischief. We need to ski down to the next station and I've got a bet that one of you will end up in a heap before we get there. Mentioning no names, Katie. 85

KATIE In that case, sir, I'll make you lose your bet.

She stands and slips. Cheers all round.

Scene Two

Night-time in the hotel – Bradley's bedroom.

Bradley, Katie, AJ, Harjit and Adiola are sitting on Bradley's bed, playing cards.

HARJIT There's no way you're going to win this game, AJ. It'll never happen.

ADIOLA Too right. *(putting down a card)* I've got the ace.

KATIE Nice one, Ad. That's got him.

AJ Oh yeah? Well, that's where you're wrong.   5

He puts down a card and they erupt with cheers, boos, screams and general mayhem. Mr Minhas enters.

MR MINHAS It sounds like a right den of iniquity in here! I'm glad you've still got the energy for such exuberance after all day on the slopes. But that's it for today, folks. You need to turn in and get a good night's sleep for tomorrow.   10
The good news is, there's more snow forecast overnight so conditions should be great for the morning.

AJ That's fine by me, sir. I reckon I'll quit this game while I'm ahead. See you. Harjit and   15
I might sneak back for a spot of serious gambling later, Brad.

| MR MINHAS | Don't even try to wind me up, AJ. Come on, off you go. |

| KATIE | Goodnight, sir. Behave yourself, Brad. Don't [20] upset Miss Farmer in the night, will you? |

She winks and they start to exit.

| BRADLEY | Cheers, everyone. We'll beat you tomorrow, AJ. |

| ADIOLA | See you, sir. Sweet dreams. |

They leave.

| MR MINHAS | This isn't a bad room, Brad. You'll get a far [25] better night on your own up here tucked out of the way. |

Katie enters with a tray, glass and bottle.

| KATIE | Look who's the lucky one. The hotel's left you a bottle of Coke out here, Brad. There's a note: 'To Brad.' Nice. See you in the morning. [30] |

She leaves the tray and exits.

| MR MINHAS | That's unusual. You must have scored a hit with someone. I've never known this place to give anything away. A bottle that size costs a fortune here. |

| BRADLEY | Or maybe I've got a rival on the ski slopes and [35] they've poisoned my drink so … what if he has? Maybe he's here. |

He takes the top off the bottle and sniffs.

MR MINHAS   Brad, you're not making much sense. Do you seriously think someone's spiked that bottle?

BRADLEY   I don't know. It's possible. The way that guy   40
swore at me and chased me back to the coach … he'd love to get a shot of poison down my throat.

MR MINHAS   Brad, I haven't got a clue what you're talking about. I reckon the mountain air must be   45
getting to you. Maybe altitude sickness is sending you doolally.

BRADLEY   Carried away? Me? Yeah, maybe …

MR MINHAS   Keep those feet of yours firmly on the ground – that's just where they need to be   50
tomorrow morning. Then it's off sight-seeing in town in the afternoon.

BRADLEY   OK, sir. Fair play. I guess I'm tired and a bit paranoid. I'll concentrate on proving to you my extra-sensational skills on the slopes in   55
the morning.

MR MINHAS   That's more like it. Sleep well. See you at breakfast. Goodnight.

Mr Minhas goes.

BRADLEY   Cheers, sir.

Bradley sits on the bed and looks around the room before staring at the bottle and sniffing it again.

He hears a noise outside his door and creeps over, slowly places his hand on the door handle, pauses, then wrenches the door open.

There is no one there.

BRADLEY I really must be tired. Time for bed.

Bradley tidies things away and brushes his teeth when there is another creak at the door and the handle moves.

Bradley quickly stuffs clothes under his duvet to make it look as though someone is sleeping there. He switches off the light and slips out through the curtains onto the balcony.

He squints back through a narrow gap in the curtains into his room … where he can see torchlights moving around. Two torches.

Without looking back, he climbs over the balcony rail, hangs from its base, swings and drops … landing neatly on the balcony below.

He does the same again, dropping down floor by floor until he reaches the ground, where he lands in the snow, brushes himself down and heads round the building to enter the hotel lobby.

Scene Three

The hotel lobby a few minutes later.

The lobby has a bar and tables where a few people sit drinking. Bradley enters and approaches the waitress at the bar, whose English is limited.

BRADLEY Excuse me, but someone's in my room. Intruders.

WAITRESS Sorry? How you mean?

BRADLEY I saw them with torches searching through my things.   5

WAITRESS Sorry, I not understand.

BRADLEY My name is Bradley Stradling and I'm in Room 42. Has anyone been asking for me? Someone sent a bottle of Coke to my room. It could be them.   10

WAITRESS Ah, yes. Bradley Stradling. I remember. A man asks for you.

BRADLEY Who was he? What did he look like?

WAITRESS Er … tall. Young. Very nice.

BRADLEY Did he have a stud in his lip?   15

WAITRESS Sorry?

BRADLEY *(miming)* A lip stud.

WAITRESS *(not understanding the mime)* The man is at that table behind you.

BRADLEY *(looking frightened and turning slowly)* No, that's 20 not him. *(relieved)* That's Karl, my ski instructor, with Steve, our coach driver. What about a man with a lip stud?

KARL *(waving)* Hi, Bradley. You not in bed yet? You need your sleep for tomorrow. 25

STEVE Don't let the teachers catch you out of your room after lights out, young man.

BRADLEY *(going to their table)* Someone was in my room just now.

STEVE Miss Farmer is patrolling the corridors. She'll 30 go ballistic if she knows you're out on the prowl – especially down here in the bar. It's out of bounds.

BRADLEY I know but I reckon it's an emergency. Something weird is going on. 35

KARL I hope you liked your drink, yes? The bottle came to your room?

BRADLEY How do you know about that, Karl?

KARL I sent it. I give one bottle each day to my star student. Today it was you. You were the 40 best. Well done.

BRADLEY Really? Oh thanks. That's a relief. In that case … I thought it was from someone else. I thought … never mind what I thought. 45

KARL   I like you, Bradley. You make me laugh.
You are quite a character.

BRADLEY   Yeah, but … so maybe the torches were only
AJ and Harjit messing about. They said they
might sneak back to my room so perhaps …   50
yeah, it all makes sense now. Thanks, Karl – I
feel better already. Cheers.

STEVE   Are you OK? You're not making much sense to
me. Now, take my advice and get up to your
room. I wouldn't like to be in your shoes if   55
Miss Farmer sees you here.

BRADLEY   Yeah, you're right. Sorry. Thanks for the drink,
Karl. See you in the morning. Goodnight,
Steve.

KARL   We'll have good snow tomorrow so get your   60
sleep.

Bradley exits.

KARL   He'll be a good skier by the end of the week.
He just needs to work on his … what is the
word?

STEVE   Attitude. That's what they all say about him.   65
Attitude. You'll see.

Blackout.

Scene Four

At breakfast the next morning.

The school party is in the hotel dining room, sitting at breakfast tables.

Bradley is sitting with Katie, AJ, Adiola and Harjit. Harjit is sleepily pouring coffees for them all.

MISS FARMER	*(entering looking serious)* Bradley, can I have a word with you, please?
BRADLEY	*(going over to her)* Yes, miss?
MISS FARMER	Sit down. I need to speak to you.
BRADLEY	That sounds scary. Have I done something wrong?
MISS FARMER	I've had a complaint. Several, in fact. Someone reported seeing you last night on your balcony. Tell me truthfully: yes or no. Did you jump down from your balcony?
BRADLEY	Yes, because someone came into my room. I thought I needed to escape.
MISS FARMER	For goodness' sake. Who was it?
BRADLEY	I'm not sure. I thought someone was trying to get me and —
MISS FARMER	Stop right there. I don't want to hear that sort of nonsense. You had absolutely no reason to

5

10

15

60

do such a foolish thing. I'm also told you were in the hotel bar after you were all sent to bed. Is that correct? **20**

BRADLEY Yes, because I was trying to —

MISS FARMER Stop again. I told you the rules. You have disobeyed yet again. And you know very well the rules concerning alcohol.

BRADLEY I didn't go to the bar for that. I wasn't **25** drinking, miss.

MISS FARMER So what's this?

Miss Farmer takes a half-empty schnapps bottle from a plastic bag.

MISS FARMER I have just found this and a packet of cigarettes in your room.

BRADLEY They're nothing to do with me. I've never seen **30** them before —

MISS FARMER Stop. When the manager of this hotel greeted me this morning with the news that someone was reported late last night swinging and shouting drunkenly from your **35** balcony while smoking and hurling abuse, I was both horrified and outraged. Surely Bradley Stradling could not have gone against all my instructions, I thought. But when I found these under your bed just now, I **40** realised your promises to me were meaningless and you had no intention of obeying my extremely clear rules.

BRADLEY   Miss, please listen. The stuff under the bed is nothing to do with me. Honest.   45

MISS FARMER   No, Bradley. Don't say 'honest' because that's clearly what you are *not*.

BRADLEY   I AM! I admit to climbing from the balcony and being down here but I was genuinely worried about an intruder. That stuff you   50
found was obviously planted in my room. I don't smoke. Ask Mr Minhas, he'll believe —

MISS FARMER   *(interrupting him)* I'm not listening to your excuses. You've really let yourself down this time. And you've let me down as well as your   55
father. Childish attention-seeking is one thing, but downright deceit is quite another.

BRADLEY   Miss, really – it's not like you think … please listen …

MISS FARMER   *(shouting as heads turn)* That's enough, Bradley.   60
I will discuss with the other staff what to do about you. I will certainly be phoning your father this evening. As for today, I'm not prepared for you to come with the rest of us on our sight-seeing and shopping afternoon   65
in Innsbruck. I will ask Karl to look after you back here. But should Karl have other plans or not wish to spend his afternoon off with a boy with an appalling attitude, I shall quite understand and will make other   70
arrangements. I will talk to you again later. In the meantime, go and sit down and reflect

on your worsening attitude before I address
the whole party about this.

*Bradley turns without speaking and sits at his
table sulkily. Katie puts an arm round him.*

KATIE What's up, Brad? What was she shouting 75
about?

BRADLEY *(seething)* I hate her. I should never have come
on this stupid trip.

KATIE Come on, don't let her upset you. You know
what she's like. 80

BRADLEY No one ever listens to my side of things.
I'm fed up with being labelled as guilty all the
time. It's not fair.

HARJIT So what's your crime this time, Brad?

BRADLEY You should know after your little stitch-up. 85
I wish you'd tell her it was only a joke.

HARJIT What are you on about?

BRADLEY It was either you or AJ. Whoever it was, you
landed me right in it.

AJ You're not making sense, Brad. What's going 90
on?

BRADLEY When you came back to my room last night I
hid out on the balcony before climbing down
the outside of the building. So I've just got
done for that, for being downstairs after hours 95
and for having booze and cigarettes in my
room. I'm grounded this afternoon and my
dad's getting 'the call'. So thanks, guys.

ADIOLA	I didn't know anyone went back to your room. What was that about?	100
HARJIT	No idea. I went straight to bed. I was well tired.	
AJ	And me. Seriously, Brad – we didn't go back to your room. Honest.	
BRADLEY	With torches. I saw you through the window.	105
HARJIT	Seriously, Brad. It wasn't us. I swear.	
BRADLEY	So where did that stuff come from under my bed?	
AJ	Not guilty, your honour.	
ADIOLA	Maybe it was already there.	110
	Everyone stares.	
ADIOLA	No. OK. That wasn't a good suggestion.	
KATIE	Poor Brad. This is a nightmare. I'll go and talk to Miss Farmer.	
BRADLEY	No. Leave her. I need to sort this out without her making it worse. I've got some thinking to do. Just as well I won't be joining you in Innsbruck, eh?	115
KATIE	Is she seriously banning you from coming with us? That's a bit harsh.	
AJ	What will we do without you? And what will you do on your own?	120
BRADLEY	I've got my life to sort out.	

*He sits with head in hands as everyone leaves.
Only Katie stays.*

KATIE   Cheer up, Brad. It'll be OK. I know what you're thinking – but that Lipstud guy wouldn't be here, would he? You'd better not mention him.   125
Miss wouldn't understand.

BRADLEY   If she tells my dad – that's it. He'll never talk to me again. I just wanted him to be proud of me for once.

He struggles to keep control. Katie puts her arm round him.

BRADLEY   I so wanted that old bag to tell him I'd   130
impressed her out here.

KATIE   Don't get upset. We'll sort it out.

BRADLEY   Dad's never thought much of me. For some reason we just can't get on. I'm sure I'm the reason he left Mum. I just seem to get   135
everything wrong all the time.

KATIE   That's not true, Brad. You can't blame yourself for all that stuff. Think positive.

BRADLEY   Yeah, I'm positive I saw someone with torches in my room and I've got to find out who it   140
was. And I'm not going to give up until I've discovered the truth. Let's face it, my whole reputation depends on it.

Blackout.

Scene Five

On the ski slopes that afternoon.

Karl and Bradley stand at the top of a tricky black run.

KARL How about it then, Brad? It's a black run with challenges but nothing too scary.

BRADLEY Yeah – I'll give it a go. I feel bad that I'm stopping you doing some really advanced stuff. It's good of you to stay behind and look 5 after me.

KARL No problem. I enjoy this. You are doing well. You have good style. You even fall over gracefully. If you do well going down here, I'll take you right up there to the cable car if you 10 like. You'll need a strong head for heights.

BRADLEY Brilliant. I'd love it.

KARL Can you see the two cable cars cross each other in the middle at the highest point over the valley? A sheer drop of hundreds of 15 metres. Many tourists pass out so there's a first aid chalet at both ends. They provide a good sit-down and a shot of brandy!

BRADLEY Don't mention alcohol. Miss Farmer thinks I've got a serious drink problem. 20

KARL I'm really sorry you have been in trouble, Brad. You seem a good kid to me. Your cousin thinks well of you, too.

BRADLEY *(frowning)* Sorry? I've never seen my cousin!

KARL But he's on holiday here. I met him last night. 25
He came into the bar with his girlfriend after you went to bed. He was telling me your dad lives in Glasgow.

BRADLEY What? Tell me … what did he look like?

KARL You don't know what your cousin looks like? 30
Not much like you, it's true.

BRADLEY No, really – this is important. Describe him to me.

KARL I don't know … quite tall, nice clothes, er … maybe twenty … 35

BRADLEY His face. Describe his face.

KARL Er … not shaved … and one of those things in his lip. A stud.

BRADLEY *(reacting with a long pause)* So … where is he now? What did he say? 40

KARL Why are you getting stressed? Aren't you pleased to see your cousin? He said they were on holiday here and wanted to catch up with you some time. I didn't speak with him much. I just told him you're in Room 42. 45
He asked whether you had a mobile phone but I didn't know.

BRADLEY So it *was* them searching with torches for my

67

phone last night. Just as well Miss Farmer confiscated it. She's got it. 50

KARL Actually, I have it now. She asked me to look after it and said you were only to use it in an emergency. I think she thought I might lose you up here. You can have it just in case you get lost – but please don't do anything stupid 55 with it.

Karl hands a scrap of paper and the phone to Bradley.

KARL Here's my number if you lose me.

BRADLEY Cheers, Karl. But my phone isn't my main worry at the minute. What about his girlfriend – what was she like? 60

KARL Charming. I spoke to her only a little. Very nice girl.

BRADLEY What did she say? What was she like?

KARL I asked her about the tattoo on the back of her hand. It's a scorpion. Like me, she's a 65 Scorpio, with a birthday in November. But why do you seem so worried?

BRADLEY Did she ask about me?

KARL Not much. She just asked what we will be doing today. So I told her you were all off to 70 Innsbruck unless anyone misbehaves.

BRADLEY So it was them! They wanted me to be kept behind. They want me on my own. I bet he's

watching me. He's probably got binoculars
fixed on me right now.   75

KARL   Hey – whoa, whoa … Steve told me you get
a bit excited now and again. Just calm it, eh?
Let's not get too stressed by all this. Let's have
a good time skiing down this black run. Tell
you what, I'll buy you a schnitzel or pastry at   80
the café as a reward for getting down in one
piece.

Karl gets into position above the slope.

BRADLEY   That's the least of my worries right now. After
what you've just told me, I think I might need
that first aid chalet and a dirty great Saint   85
Bernard's barrel of brandy.

They ski off down the mountain.

Scene Six

A mountain café half an hour later.

Bradley and Karl arrive at a table in the café, clomping in their ski boots and carrying trays.

KARL   We have a choice of tables for once.
It's getting quite late. It will be dark in an hour.

BRADLEY   I am so shattered I can hardly stand. But
that was awesome, Karl. My heart was in my
mouth at the steep, icy bit. I just wish I could   5
ski as well as you. And the way you do those
jumps is just amazing.

They sit at a table.

KARL   Years of practice. You did well to keep going.
You've got good leg muscle strength. It shows
that you do gymnastics and keep fit.   10

BRADLEY   I won't be fit after this massive pastry. Thanks
for this, Karl. You've been brilliant. To be
honest, this is far better than shopping in
Innsbruck.

KARL   I agree. It's perfect weather today. Just look at   15
that glorious orange sun going down behind
the mountains. We've just got time to head up
to the cable car and enjoy the sunset over the
glaciers.

BRADLEY Magic. So is this pastry!   20

> *A woman wearing large, dark ski goggles,*
> *gloves, scarf and a hood approaches them. She*
> *has a strong American accent but she is, in fact,*
> *Lipstud's girlfriend. She is well disguised.*

GIRLFRIEND Excuse me for butting in, you guys … but do
either of you happen to speak German?

KARL Yes. Can I help?

GIRLFRIEND I hope so. My father is unwell outside and I'm
trying to explain to the guy on the lift that   25
we need help getting him up to the first aid
chalet. Would you mind?

KARL No problem. *(standing)* I won't be long, Brad.
Enjoy your pastry – you've got most of it over
your face!   30

> *Karl follows the woman outside while Bradley*
> *continues to eat alone. Shortly the woman returns.*

GIRLFRIEND Listen, I'm so sorry about this. My father really
isn't well and your friend has kindly offered
to take him up to the chalet to deal with all
the German speaking up there. I'm just so
hopeless at languages.   35

BRADLEY OK. Actually, Karl was about to take me up
there to go on the cable car. I wonder why he
didn't ask me to go with him.

GIRLFRIEND Well, actually he did. He asked me to look after
you and to follow him up the mountain in the   40
ski lift. They'll be in a car just ahead of us.

BRADLEY In that case, I'd better finish this pastry and we can get up to the summit. I'm really looking forward to what I'm going to find up there.

GIRLFRIEND I'm sure you are. *(aside, in a low voice)* You'll be really surprised. 45

Bradley follows her outside.

Scene Seven

In a gondola ski lift.

The gondola ski lift is a four-seater but only the woman and Bradley are inside, sitting side by side.

GIRLFRIEND I just love these mountains but this lift is a bit scary, the way it swings out over the treetops down there.

BRADLEY Heights never really bother me. I love climbing up things. I'd like to do real rock-climbing   5 when I'm older. We've got a climbing wall in our school sports hall and Mr Minhas says I'm like Spiderman with a hyperactivity disorder.

GIRLFRIEND Really? Hey, it looks like everyone's coming down the mountain and we're the only ones   10 going up. It's getting really cold too. Are you cold, Bradley?

BRADLEY Yes, a bit. *(looking puzzled)* Er … how do you know my name?

GIRLFRIEND Your German friend told me. Look, I've got a   15 flask of coffee in my rucksack. How about if you have a sip to warm you up? I absolutely insist you have some after I stopped you finishing your drink back there. It's the least I can do to repay you …   20

She takes out a flask and removes her gloves. Bradley sees the scorpion tattoo on the back of her hand and stares, transfixed.

GIRLFRIEND Are you OK, honey? You've gone very quiet. Here, drink this …

She passes him a cup of coffee.

BRADLEY Thanks.

He takes it but continues to stare ahead, in deep thought.

GIRLFRIEND Say, honey, would you happen to have a cell phone with you? Mine doesn't work and I'd just like to give my father a call to check he's OK.

BRADLEY Er … *(touching his phone in his pocket)* no, sorry. My teacher took my phone off me. She told me I wasn't allowed to use it and —

GIRLFRIEND Not to worry right now. Say, aren't you going to drink that while it's hot?

BRADLEY Yeah.

He takes a sip and looks at the coffee blankly before pointing up the mountain.

BRADLEY Is that the cable car station just there?

He empties the cup on the floor while she looks out the window.

GIRLFRIEND Sure.

BRADLEY It looks like we'll soon be there. I can't see Karl anywhere. It's getting quite late.

25

30

35

He fiddles with his watch, surreptitiously setting the alarm.

BRADLEY It'll soon be dark.

GIRLFRIEND Wow, that's good – you've finished the coffee. Perfect. 40

She takes the cup back.

BRADLEY I'm sorry, but I don't feel very well. *(putting his head in his hands)* For some reason I'm getting really tired and I think I'm …

Bradley slumps forward onto the floor.

GIRLFRIEND *(speaking on her phone, now in her normal voice)* It's worked. He drank the lot and he's sleeping like a baby. Get ready to help me lift him out – 45 in about thirty seconds.

As she speaks, Bradley slips off his watch and slides it under her seat.

GIRLFRIEND He hasn't got his phone but we can get that from his teacher's room tonight.

Suddenly, the watch's cockerel alarm goes off under her seat; she is startled and distracted, looking underneath.

As the doors open, Bradley sees his chance to escape.

Scene Eight

Outside the first aid chalet near the cable car station.

The icy area at the top of the mountain is almost deserted and the first aid chalet is already closed.

Bradley dives out of the slowing gondola ski lift, dodges past Lipstud and runs to the chalet, as Lipstud's girlfriend shouts after him from the still-moving ski lift. She clambers out and runs to Lipstud, who stands with a rucksack next to a wheelchair – in which Karl is slumped, unconscious.

LIPSTUD I thought you said you'd drugged the kid.

GIRLFRIEND He tricked me.

LIPSTUD This is the last time he'll get the better of either of us. Stay here with the wheelchair. I hired it from first aid. I told them the guy had 5 fainted. But I don't care about him. It's that kid I want now. There's a tiny dose left in the syringe. Enough to knock him out to get him in the cable car.

> *He heads to the chalet, where Bradley is crouching round the corner.*

BRADLEY *(texting Katie)* CALL ME NOW. Bx 10

> *He does not send the text but stuffs the phone in his pocket.*

He looks for somewhere to run for help but there are only a couple of attendants left on the mountain top. Before Bradley can run to them, Lipstud grabs him and plunges the syringe into his arm.

LIPSTUD   Sleep well, you annoying little brat.

BRADLEY   Aaah! *(trying to break free)* Help is on its way so you won't be able to —

LIPSTUD   Wrong. They've just closed the ski lift. The good news is that we've got this place to ourselves. The bad news is that only two out of the four of us will be going down again – alive. Unlucky.
15

BRADLEY   But I need to …

Bradley slumps.

LIPSTUD   *(calling to his girlfriend)* Bring over the wheelchair.
20

She brings the wheelchair with Karl in it. Lipstud pushes it to the edge of a steep drop and tips Karl out, who falls down the slope into a pile of snow.

GIRLFRIEND   *(gesturing towards Karl)* How long before he wakes up?

LIPSTUD   He won't. He'll freeze to death overnight. By the time they find him, we'll be heading home. I just want to make sure we get rid of the kid once and for all. This is all going even better than I'd planned.
25

The two of them lift Bradley into the wheelchair and casually wheel him into the cable car. There are no other passengers, just the three of them.

The doors close and the cable car slowly moves out over the cliff, with a sheer drop below them.

The other cable car on the far summit sets off at the same time, slowly heading towards them.

The sun is sinking below the mountain tops.

Scene Nine

Inside the cable car – high above a ravine.

Bradley begins to stir in the wheelchair. Lipstud slides open the window and then faces him.

Lipstud's girlfriend sits beside the wheelchair, staring aggressively at Bradley.

LIPSTUD Before we throw him out, I've got to know about my photo on his phone. I must be certain he hasn't sent it to anyone. Make sure you wake him up.

GIRLFRIEND *(shaking Bradley's shoulders)* Wake up, you idiot … *(tapping his face)* come on, wake up. You need to talk. 5

BRADLEY *(opening his eyes)* What do you want? What are you doing?

LIPSTUD You're a fool. You refused my offer at the airport. No one ever refuses me. If you'd agreed to help, you'd have been part of our mission. You'd be a comrade in the struggle rather than the enemy. All enemies must be destroyed. 10

GIRLFRIEND You should never have taken his picture. Big mistake. 15

BRADLEY *(blinking and starting to focus)* I could tell when I first met you there was something odd about

79

you. I mean, something scarily weird. Evil,
even. I know you're planning something mad. **20**
Something where people will get hurt. I'm
right, aren't I? I tried to warn them about you
at the airport. You don't care if people die.

LIPSTUD Just collateral damage. Besides, the ignorant
deserve to perish. Just as your school party **25**
was going to die because of you. At least
you've saved them from that. Now we've got
the prize in our possession.

BRADLEY What do you mean?

GIRLFRIEND There's no need to tell him all that. Let's just **30**
get rid of him and we can go home. I don't like
it in here.

*She takes a small vial of poison from her pocket
and fills a syringe.*

LIPSTUD Wait. I want this kid to know just what a
fool he's been. He thinks he's clever but he's
not. I believe in making people face their **35**
ignorance. *(bringing his face up close to Bradley's)*
I'm the clever one. I was the brightest at
university – until I was told to leave because
they didn't like my views. Too extreme, they
said. Too radical. Too clever to handle. Genius **40**
is never recognised by the ignorant.

GIRLFRIEND They couldn't face the truth. Only I could see
the vision. You can tell I was the smartest
drama student in my year. I had you fooled
with my American character. **45**

80

BRADLEY Only at first. You couldn't disguise your hand tattoo so you can't be that clever.

GIRLFRIEND *(striking him)* Don't argue with us. *(to Lipstud)* I see what you mean by this kid's attitude. Let me inject him now. He's so infuriating. 50

LIPSTUD Jab him in a minute when we get to the maximum drop in the middle of the ravine. Give him longer to fall. With the poison, it'll be belt and braces. Death guaranteed.

BRADLEY You could have killed me while I was drowsy 55 just now – so why didn't you?

LIPSTUD I want answers first.

BRADLEY Same here. What did you mean about my school party going to die? What are you planning? What have my friends done to 60 upset you?

GIRLFRIEND Let's just get this over with. He asks too many questions.

She holds up the syringe and checks it.

LIPSTUD *(snapping at her)* Leave it to me. *(turning back to Bradley)* If you hadn't walked so easily into 65 this trap today, I had 'plan b' ready. *(holding up his rucksack)* I found out from your driver that tonight everyone is going to the bowling alley by coach. Just a few of these packs of TATP strapped to the exhaust system would 70 do the job. Better known as triacetone triperoxide, this little lot would heat up as the

coach trundled along the mountain road …
then BOOM. Everyone would be blown to
smithereens – you and your phone and its   75
images included. Problem solved.

BRADLEY You've got those explosives in that rucksack?
You are totally mad.

GIRLFRIEND *(shouting in his face)* Not mad! He is extremely
clever, with an incredible IQ.   80

BRADLEY Well, if you're so clever, why are you carrying
that stuff around with you up here? They told
us in science about those types of explosives.
They're very unstable.

LIPSTUD Exactly. I wouldn't want to leave them lying   85
around. But up here in the snow and cold this
stuff is very stable. It's only heat and friction
that sets it off.

BRADLEY Is that the stuff you hid in my bag on the
plane to Glasgow?   90

GIRLFRIEND Enough of your questions. You don't need to
know any more.

LIPSTUD No, I'll tell him. Not that he'll understand.
He's a kid with a father who actually bothers
to collect him from an airport. Nothing like   95
mine – whom I despise.

BRADLEY Are you blaming your dad for screwing you
up?

LIPSTUD *(almost screaming)* YES! You've got no idea
what it's like for me, being abandoned and   100

disowned by a billionaire megalomaniac father. I was left to grow up in squalor, to struggle all my life – how do you think that feels? When he owns airlines, hotel chains and half the planet but he's never given me a penny. Nothing. The only thing he's given me is lousy genes and a lifetime in hospitals.

105

GIRLFRIEND   A serious blood disorder, if you must know.

BRADLEY   More like a serious mental disorder, if you ask me.

110

GIRLFRIEND   *(grabbing Bradley by the throat)* It's not a joke. It's been a life of struggle but you kids who have everything with cushy, dead-easy lives don't know what it's like.

115

LIPSTUD   Exactly. Kids who go skiing with *(mockingly)* 'very nice daddies who give them all they want' deserve to face up to what it's really like. *(bringing his nose close to Bradley's and whispering dangerously)* Your type hasn't got a clue. But you soon will.

120

BRADLEY   *(pulling away and standing to cross the car, gaining confidence but also becoming angry)* Hold on a minute. Who says I've had a cushy life? I had loads of health problems as a little kid too, if you must know. And I don't happen to live with my dad, who – let's face it – doesn't exactly like me or want to spend much time with me. His work matters to him

125

far more than I do. But you don't find me
getting all stressy about it and beating up
any kid who upsets me. Not often, anyway. 130

LIPSTUD *(still mocking, as he paces the cable car)* Oh,
you poor little boy. My heart bleeds for
you. My whole body bleeds – that's the
problem. That's my inheritance. A life of blood
transfusions. What do you think that's like? 135

BRADLEY I blame my dad for rubbish genes too.
And, actually, I often feel abandoned and
rejected by my dad. But that doesn't make me
want to blow up the world, does it?

LIPSTUD *(shouting, enraged)* Don't contradict me! No 140
one ever contradicts me.

GIRLFRIEND Keep calm. Don't let this scum kid upset you.
He's not worth it. He's disposable. Let me
eradicate him. *(touching his neck)* You need to
de-stress. 145

LIPSTUD *(turning on her, angrily)* Stop patronising me!
(turning to Bradley) Listen, kid. I despise
everything about you. Especially your
attitude. I should never have spoken to you
on that plane. 150

BRADLEY So you made a mistake? That just goes to
show you can't be that clever after all.

LIPSTUD *(striking him)* Don't make fun of me. I will
not be mocked. No one is allowed to
criticise me. 155

GIRLFRIEND Because he's always right. *(whispering to Bradley)* Don't torment him.

BRADLEY So you're taking out your revenge for an unhappy childhood on me and everyone else.

LIPSTUD It was far more than unhappy. My father despised me. 160

BRADLEY I know the feeling. But when you grow up you have to deal with all that stuff and take responsibility for your own actions without blaming everyone else for the rubbish in the 165 past. That's my advice, mate.

GIRLFRIEND The last thing he needs is advice from you. Our fight is to strike back at the powers of ignorance and greed.

BRADLEY Fight? So what does that mean, exactly? 170 Blowing up innocent people?

LIPSTUD No one is innocent! It's a fight we're determined to win. Revenge and change. We fight oppression and exploitation. That's what we stand for. 175

BRADLEY *(looking at the door and edging towards it)* So what's that got to do with getting me to carry explosives at the airport? How's that going to help your fight? I know I'm only a kid, but to me it looks like you're one big, angry guy with 180 an even bigger attitude problem than mine.

LIPSTUD It's nothing to do with attitude. It's vengeance. I'm going to ruin my father like he ruined me.

85

And all capitalist scum like him. Every one of his aircraft, trains and multinational companies will be destroyed one by one. Then he'll know what it's like to suffer like I've had to. He'll take notice of me then.   185

BRADLEY And I thought I had issues with my dad! So how do you pay for all this stuff?   190

LIPSTUD Contacts. Nothing is going to stop me and I'll kill whoever it takes to achieve my goal. I've been planning this all my life and I'm nearly there at last.

GIRLFRIEND *(peering out of the window)* Let's jab him and   195
throw him out here. Get it over with.

LIPSTUD *(ignoring her)* Next weekend I'll deliver the last supplies of TATP to airports, railway terminals and hotels for assembling all the bombs. You'd hear all about it on the world news – if   200
you were still alive. But you won't be. You're coming over here …

He drags Bradley by the scruff of the neck to the open window and pushes his head outside.

BRADLEY And they reckon I've got attitude problems!

GIRLFRIEND Hardly anyone will hear about your accident – just a line in the papers: 'Boy and ski instructor   205
killed in fall.' No one will know the truth or that you'd ever met us.

Bradley struggles free and darts to the other side of the car.

BRADLEY That's where you're wrong.

> *Lipstud hurls himself at Bradley and wrestles with him on the floor.*

LIPSTUD I'm never wrong.

BRADLEY *(Lipstud pinning him down)* I took your photo,   210
remember? *(quickly inventing a story)* I sent it to
my dad and he's gone to the police. They now
know what the Eurotunnel smuggler of TATP
looks like.

> *Lipstud suddenly jumps up in a rage, kicking and thumping at the sides of the car.*

LIPSTUD *(shouting at his girlfriend)* You said it would be   215
all right! You said this wouldn't happen!

GIRLFRIEND He's bluffing. *(hissing at Bradley)* Stop upsetting
him! Keep things calm. Don't make him mad.
Not in here. Not with his blood pressure.

> *She lifts the syringe.*

LIPSTUD *(pacing manically)* I need to destroy his phone.   220
Where is it?

BRADLEY My teacher took it off me …

> *He touches the phone in his pocket, surreptitiously sending Katie the text and sliding the phone into the wheelchair.*

LIPSTUD Come here, kid. *(grabbing Bradley by the neck)*
We're nearly above the middle of the ravine.
This is where you die. You can either step   225
out through this window peacefully or …

(grabbing a distress flare from an emergency pack mounted on the wall) I'll fire this in your face and you'll fall burning and screaming. The choice is yours.

GIRLFRIEND *(lunging forward and stabbing the syringe into Bradley's shoulder)* But there's no choice about 230
this. Euthanasia … with the best view in the world. A view to die for.

> *Bradley winces as the needle is removed, then breaks free and looks out through the open window, the wind in his face.*

BRADLEY I'm going to do this my way …

> *He jumps up on the seat, puts one foot on the window ledge and reaches up to grab the outside rail above the window.*

> *Suddenly his phone goes off, in a burst of loud rifle shots. Lipstud and his girlfriend spin round, startled.*

> *By the time they look back to Bradley, he has gone. He is clambering out onto the roof of the cable car.*

> *Lipstud runs to the window and sees Bradley's foot dangling above him. He grabs it and there is a tussle until Lipstud's girlfriend hands him a distress flare.*

GIRLFRIEND Get him with this – quick!

LIPSTUD My pleasure. Your time is up, kid … 235

Lipstud aims the flare and fires but Bradley kicks at it, shooting it back inside the cable car, which instantly fills with a shower of red smoke.

Bradley rolls across the roof of the cable car, grabs the central pillar and pulls himself to his feet. He positions himself to leap across to the other cable car which is now drawing level.

Just as he jumps, the flare inside the cable car smashes into Lipstud's rucksack. Smoke and sparks fly before it ignites and erupts. A massive explosion rips the cable car apart in a ball of flame and flying debris.

Bradley, lit up by the huge flash, clings to the roof of the other cable car, his legs dangling over the side. He looks over his shoulder at the falling wreckage and smoke.

BRADLEY Wow!

Blackout.

Scene Ten

Hospital – days later.

Bradley, attached to a drip, is lying on a bed, with his leg in plaster and his neck in a collar. Karl is in the next bed.

The doctor and two medical staff are at Bradley's bedside.

DOCTOR *(examining Bradley's medical notes)* You are doing remarkably well, young man … under the circumstances. When they first brought you in, we were very concerned. We had a number of scares, I can tell you.   5

BRADLEY To be honest, I don't remember a thing.

MEDIC 1 Just as well. Here is your medication.

The medic gives Bradley some pills and a drink.

DOCTOR The blood transfusion and medication saved you. That poison they injected into you would have caused major organ failure in a matter   10 of days. But we've managed to flush out your system and we've prevented any permanent damage. All the other bumps and cracks are doing fine. I'll see you again tomorrow.

The doctor exits.

MEDIC 2 *(attending to Bradley's drip)* I told your mother
to get some rest. She said she'll be back to see
you at lunchtime.   15

BRADLEY Thanks. Lunchtime – how long's that? I'm
feeling a lot better but I haven't got a clue
what time or day it is. It's really weird.   20

MEDIC 1 That's quite normal. Your body clock has
had a shaking. You were in intensive care for
twenty-four hours then in here for two days.
It's Saturday breakfast time.

MEDIC 2 *(turning to Karl)* Your breakfast is on the trolley.   25
You should be able to serve yourself now.
Hopefully, after another day of observation
you'll be able to go home, Karl.

   The medics exit.

KARL Did I hear that your father is flying over?

BRADLEY Yeah. Would you believe my mum's only just   30
told him what's happened? Mind you, she's
actually spoken to him. This is a week of
miracles!

   AJ, Katie, Adiola and Harjit enter with gifts.

KARL Look who's here. Your little fan club.

BRADLEY You're skiving! You lot should be up there   35
skiing on those mountains.

KATIE *(giving him a gentle hug)* We've finished – we're
about to go home. Brad, I've been so worried

about you. Talking on the phone isn't the
same as seeing you at last. How are you?   40

BRADLEY   Good, thanks. The ankle doesn't hurt now
and I really don't need this collar thing. They
go a bit over the top if you ask me. And now
my blood seems to be OK, too. It was Karl
who got the big-time concussion when they   45
tipped him over the edge. I really thought he
was a goner. That's until I blacked out!

ADIOLA   So how did they find poor old Karl in the dark?

KARL   Once more, it was Brad to the rescue. A clever
lad, I think.   50

BRADLEY   Hardly. When I eventually got off that cable
car after my 'ride of hell', I found an attendant
who called for help. That's when I fell on the
ice and hurt my ankle. But … and this was my
cunning plan …   55

HARJIT   *(doing a drum-roll on the bedside locker)* Oh no,
not a cunning plan!

AJ   *(also suitably dramatic)* Do tell us – what was
this cunning plan?

BRADLEY   No more than Karl's phone number. He'd   60
given it to me earlier. But, as my phone had
been blown to smithereens, I got this guy
to call on his phone while I listened. Lo and
behold, coming from somewhere below us
in the icy darkness was a muffled bleeping.   65
That's how the rescue guys found him. They

actually airlifted us by helicopter which was well cool. Better than skiing down.

KARL Not that I knew anything about it. But that phone call saved my life. 70

BRADLEY No, Karl. It was another call that saved both our lives. It was the wonderful Katie. Give us another drum roll, Harjit. *(he does)* Katie is the star in all this.

KATIE Why? What did I do? 75

BRADLEY If you hadn't replied to my text and phoned me back immediately, my M14 rifle ringtone wouldn't have gone off. That gave me the valuable seconds I needed to climb out of the cable car and escape the blast. 80

ADIOLA So how exactly did you get so sick? Miss said you nearly …

BRADLEY Snuffed it? Yeah. I began feeling all weird inside the helicopter. Luckily they had a mobile life-support machine thing – they've 85 told me I stopped breathing. Lipstud's girlfriend jabbed me with a fatal dose of some kind of morphine or something. It kills you in twenty minutes if you don't get special treatment. 90

KATIE That's terrible. You need another hug …

Katie and Bradley kiss, to cheers, whistles and whoops as she slides a note under his pillow.

Miss Farmer enters with Mr Minhas.

MISS FARMER Whatever is all this noise? I don't think you should be kissing the patient, Katie. You might upset his blood pressure! Can you four just wait outside for a few minutes as we're a bit of 95 a crowd. Go and get some chips or something and come back soon, eh?

AJ OK, miss – we know when we're not wanted.

ADIOLA See you in a bit, Brad.

HARJIT We've brought a pack of cards for later. 100

KATIE We won't be long … my hero!

AJ and Harjit groan.

AJ, Harjit, Adiola and Katie exit.

MR MINHAS How are you two feeling today?

KARL Much better, thanks.

BRADLEY Fine, sir.

MR MINHAS Do you know, Bradley, I've only just realised 105 what you did up there on that cable car. The police have shown us all kinds of pictures. How did you do all that stuntman stuff?

BRADLEY All down to my amazing gym teacher, I guess.

MR MINHAS But whatever possessed you even to consider 110 leaping from one cable car to another? It was a crazy idea.

BRADLEY The alternative was just a wee bit fatal. It's amazing what a bit of panic and adrenaline can do! Mind you, I wasn't too happy with 115 my performance, I'm afraid, sir. For a straddle

jump, it was pretty poor on style, poise and
follow-through. You wouldn't have been
impressed with my 'clinging on for dear life'
skills either.   120

MISS FARMER From now on Bradley Stradling will always be
known as Bradley Straddle Jump!

MR MINHAS Just as soon as you get that ankle back to
strength you can re-enact the whole event
for us for the DVD I'm shooting of this trip.   125

BRADLEY Can I have a safety-net this time?

MISS FARMER Bradley, I need to tell you again how
amazed I am about what happened and
what you did. I never thought I would hear
myself say this but I should have believed   130
you back at the hotel and I'm sorry I didn't.
You've been very brave and apparently all the
newspapers back home are desperate to get
your story. There's already a crowd of
reporters camped outside this hospital.   135

BRADLEY I bet you never thought I'd be famous one
day, miss. Especially that time at parents'
evening when all this started.

MISS FARMER I think we've all learned a lot since then,
Bradley. And I'm sure when we all get back   140
we can have a fresh start. Hopefully a new
attitude for both of us. No more fighting or
swearing from you and I'll try not to blame
you for everything.

BRADLEY That would be cool.   145

MISS FARMER You've got a good brain, Bradley. You just
need to use it.

BRADLEY I reckon I gave it quite a bit of use up that
mountain! My brain cells were working
overtime in that cable car, I can tell you. High   150
altitude must be good for my brain. So maybe
you might even let me come on the trip
next year?

MISS FARMER You're already at the top of the list. Now,
I understand your father is about to arrive   155
so you'll want to spend some time with him
before I talk to him. Maybe if we take Karl
outside for a spot of breakfast, we'll come
back and see you just before we have to head
back home. Hopefully it won't be long until   160
you're home, too.

*They exit as a bedside phone rings. Bradley
answers.*

BRADLEY Hi, Katie. Yeah, I can talk as much as you
want – no one else is here at the minute.
(pause) You did what? Where?

*Bradley looks under his pillow and finds a note
from her.*

BRADLEY Yes, I've found it. That was a sneaky move. I   165
didn't see you put it there. Thanks – I'll read
it when no one's watching. *(pause)* You what?
You were up all night thinking of me and
writing to me? You're such a star – and I miss
you too. Thanks, Katie. See you soon. Bye.   170

He begins to read her letter but quickly hides it when he hears someone coming. It is his father, carrying chocolates. When he sees Bradley, he pauses and is temporarily lost for words.

DAD   Brad, I don't know what to say.

They hug, his dad patting Bradley's shoulder.

BRADLEY   Nor do I, Dad.

DAD   That's a first then. You've normally got lots to say. Usually too much!

BRADLEY   Thanks for coming all this way. It's so good to   175
see you.

DAD   I'd have come far sooner if I'd known. You're looking great. I expected … *(struggling to keep control)* You're a great son, Brad. I mean it.

BRADLEY   *(taken aback)* Really?   180

DAD   Really. How are you feeling?

BRADLEY   I'll bounce back. I told you my trampolining was good for something. I'll soon be back and annoying you again. In fact, you've got those socks on again, Dad. Gross!   185

DAD   I didn't want to disappoint you. So … are you managing all right? I mean, are you OK with everything? No major worries now?

BRADLEY   I'm fine, Dad. Everything's fine. I'm very lucky.

DAD   It's more than luck, Brad. You've done   190
wonders – despite … despite all I've said.
I'm sorry if I … the thing is, you've done

something amazing. You only told me the half
of it on the phone …

BRADLEY Don't worry, Dad – I'm going to keep 195
repeating every single detail to you at every
parents' evening from now on. I want to tell
you lots of other stuff too – but I don't really
know how to say it. I'm not really sure how to
put it … *(struggling to speak and keep control)* 200

DAD It's OK, Brad. I guess we've both got things we
need to tell each other.

BRADLEY I'm sorry I've given you a bit of a hard time
lately. I know I haven't always helped matters.
It's just that … I've been thinking … 205

DAD Same here, Brad. I've been thinking a lot and
I'm sorry for a whole pile of stuff.

BRADLEY We're going to be OK now, aren't we, Dad?
I mean, you and I.

DAD Yeah. We'll be just fine. 210

They embrace again.

BRADLEY We don't normally do hugs, do we? Dad,
I'm sorry I've been … you know, difficult
sometimes. I've had a lot of time to think in
here in the middle of the night. And I've never
even said thanks for paying for this trip and 215
stuff. For everything.

DAD Sometimes it takes something scary like this
to make us all think. I realise how I haven't
always been there for you and maybe I've

been a bit too critical at times. The thing is, 220
I just want the best for you but I do things
wrong sometimes. And do you know what?
It was just the same with me and my dad. We
never got on and now he's gone I can't ever
put things right. But *we* can, Brad. You and I. 225
I know I haven't been a great dad and I should
never have said some things. I've even just
tried to say sorry to your mother. It's the first
conversation we've had without yelling our
heads off. 230

BRADLEY Well, I guess that's a step in the right direction.

DAD The scary thing is – you're so like me, Brad.
We flare up without stopping to think first.
Your fights and swearing and arguing with
teachers won't get you anywhere. It didn't 235
with me as a kid, either – apart from getting
me the cane.

BRADLEY *(smiling and imitating him)* And that never did
you any harm!

DAD To be honest, it probably did. It probably 240
made me the bitter and twisted old so-and-so
I am today.

BRADLEY Not as bitter and twisted as that mad guy
who wanted to blow us all up. He was
seriously deranged, I reckon. And he blamed 245
everything on his father.

DAD Really? It seems dads have a lot to answer for.

BRADLEY Yeah, but I think some sons can be a bit of a pain too. That's what I've been thinking about lying here. You see, Dad – I've always blamed 250 you for all kinds of stuff but that's not really fair, is it? Let's face it, I don't want to end up like him, do I?

DAD What, dead?

BRADLEY Bitter, twisted and screwed-up – a total raving 255 nutcase.

DAD Too late, Brad. You've already got the full set! But now you listen to me. I need to say this right now. I need to speak my mind and I really mean it. *(pausing)* I'm dead proud of you, son. 260

He looks away, unable to speak momentarily.

BRADLEY Seriously? You've … no one has ever said that to me before.

DAD Well, I genuinely mean it. Gran's proud of you, too. She's gone a bit wild, of course.

BRADLEY Oh no, what's she done now? 265

DAD She went straight online and ordered you a solar-powered model cable car – complete with daft sound effects and flashing lights.

BRADLEY *(laughing)* Good old Gran – though I don't need sound effects to remind me of that guy's 270 bomb. You should have heard it go off. I really thought …

DAD Served the blighter right. Nothing like being hoist by his own petard.

BRADLEY What? *(laughing loudly)* What's that supposed   275
to mean?

DAD Blown up by his own device. The expression is
in Shakespeare. *Hamlet*, I think.

BRADLEY Wow! What it is to have a clever dad. I'm well
impressed.   280

Bradley opens the chocolates and they both
take one. They are now far more relaxed.

DAD So now you know where you get it from.
Seriously though, this maniac you stopped in
his tracks was set on really evil stuff.
The police back home told me they've traced
him and searched his address. Apparently   285
his shed is jammed full of explosive devices
and all kinds of dangerous things. He was
planning a lot of mad schemes. Some kind of
anarchist extremist by all accounts.

BRADLEY Exactly what I tried to tell everyone when I   290
first met him. It looks like even Miss Farmer
might forgive me now. Have you spoken to
her yet?

DAD We had a brief word.

BRADLEY So what's the verdict? Have we progressed   295
from last parents' evening? *(imitating her voice*
brilliantly) 'Bradley is going to change for the
better, you mark my words. I now see him as
my own personal challenge. Leave it with me.
We're in for a major epiphany with this young   300

man. I feel it in my bones.' I feel my epiphany in my ankle bone right now! Just a twinge.

DAD *(laughing)* You sound just like her. But it looks as if Miss Farmer was right. You've certainly changed, Brad. We both have. And it's going to be different now. Even so, I still think I can sum you up in a nutshell. 305

BRADLEY *(acting bored)* Yeah, yeah, whatever …

Bradley grins cheekily, waiting for a reaction.

DAD Just one word sums you up, as always. It begins with 'A' and ends in 'titude'. 310

BRADLEY Oh no, don't go on about attitude here, Dad. Please don't go there. I've had just about enough of that particular word.

DAD *(smiling)* Me too. That's why I've changed my mind. The word I had in mind was ALTITUDE. Let's face it, Brad, you've gone to the summit in my estimation. After all, you've become an absolute hero high up in the mountains! 315

With his hand over his face, Bradley sinks back in his pillow with a massive groan.

Blackout.

CURTAIN

Extreme Survival

By Christopher Edge

If you're stuck in an extreme situation with little chance of survival, you need a hero by your side. In harsh environments such as the icy wastes of Antarctica or deep in the Amazon jungle, a hero's survival skills can mean the difference between life and death.

Antarctic endurance

The Antarctic explorer, Sir Ernest Shackleton, was an inspirational hero who led his crew on an epic journey of survival. In 1914 he set out on an expedition to lead the first crossing of the vast Antarctic continent.

This expedition would become legendary – but not because Shackleton made the first Antarctic crossing. As Shackleton approached Antarctica, his ship, the *Endurance*, became trapped in the pack-ice. The ship began to sink and Shackleton and his men were forced to abandon the *Endurance* and take their chances on the floating ice.

Stranded

Without any modern-day radios, satellites or GPS technology, there was no way Shackleton could let the outside world know what had happened. They were hundreds of miles from safety with no hope of rescue. The ice on which they stood was a thin crust above the freezing Antarctic seas.

For six long months Shackleton and his men camped on the ice, battling to survive. They were cut off from civilisation with only limited supplies of food and essential equipment. As the food began to run low, Shackleton ordered his men to shoot and eat their dogs.

A dangerous voyage

As spring arrived, the pack-ice began to break up and Shackleton launched the three lifeboats he had rescued from the ship. Crammed into these boats, Shackleton and his crew spent seven exhausting days at sea. Finally, they landed at Elephant Island, an uninhabited island over a thousand kilometres from civilisation.

Accompanied by five of his crew, Shackleton set out again in one of the lifeboats. His goal was to reach the island of South Georgia, where help could be found. On their 17-day voyage, Shackleton and his crew battled against:

- freezing conditions;
- force 9 gales;
- gigantic waves;
- extreme hunger.

Eventually Shackleton and his men reached South Georgia, but they *still* weren't safe.

Mountain march

Stormy weather had forced Shackleton to land on the southern side of the island. To get help, they needed to reach the whaling station on the north side. An exhausted Shackleton led his men across the island's unexplored mountains and glaciers. They marched for more than 30 hours without stopping for sleep before finally reaching the whaling station.

Shackleton then borrowed a ship and returned to Elephant Island to rescue the rest of the expedition crew. He had achieved the impossible and brought every single one of his men back alive.

Survival skills

You might never need to survive on the Antarctic ice, but you still could find yourself in need of some survival skills. Lost in a forest and it's starting to get dark? Caught in a storm and need to take shelter? Get yourself out of the elements. Wind, rain and cold will sap your energy, so take shelter as quickly as you can.

Build a sixty-second shelter

If you need to build a shelter in a hurry, here's one you can make in just one minute.

- Stretch a strong cord between two trees and hang a tarpaulin or plastic sheet over it.

- Hold down the edges of the tarpaulin with heavy stones.

- Cover the ground beneath your shelter with a bed of leaves.

Remember to:

- Build your shelter on solid ground. Avoid muddy places or locations that might flood.

- Make sure your shelter has its back to the wind. This will help to keep it warm.

- Keep some ventilation. Don't build your shelter so that it is completely enclosed.

You could practise building this type of shelter in your back garden using a washing line. Can you beat 60 seconds? Why not have a competition with your friends to see who can make the shelter in the quickest time.

Emergency shelters

If you don't have the materials for a 60-second shelter or the weather is just too bad to build one, you'll need to find somewhere else to shelter.

- **Caves**: A cave can give you instant shelter, but you'll need to make sure it is safe. Check that there aren't any signs of recent rockfalls or wild animals that call the cave their home. Most caves are cold and damp, but you can build a campfire to keep yourself warm. Make sure you build this away from the entrance of the cave to stop smoke being blown inside.

- **Trees:** You can create a temporary shelter using a fallen tree. Lash a large broken branch to the trunk of the tree to make a rough tripod structure. You can weave smaller branches into this and pile up earth around the base to give you extra warmth and protection. Alternatively, build a shelter in a hollow next to a fallen tree by propping a lean-to roof made out of branches and leaves against the trunk.

- **Snow**: You might want to escape from a snowstorm, but you can build a shelter using snow itself. One way to do this is to look for a tree with low branches where the snow has built up around them. Dig down carefully to find a natural hollow beneath these branches. If the snow has drifted, you could also tunnel into a snow bank to make a cave. Hollow out an area big enough to shelter in and then use blocks of snow to cover the entrance from the elements. Remember to make air holes to stop poisonous carbon monoxide building up inside your shelter. Use a stick to poke through these air holes regularly to make sure they stay open.

Jungle survival

When Loic Pillois and Guilhem Nayral got lost on a hike in the Amazon jungle, their survival skills helped to save their lives. They built a bivouac shelter from leaves and branches and lived in it for three weeks. After their food ran out, they ate snakes, beetles, frogs and tarantulas to survive!

We would like to thank the following school and students for all their help in developing and trialling *Ski Jump*.

Biggar High School:

Alasdair Brown
Hollie Brown
Sean Christie
Andrew Colgan
Daniel Cummings
Nathan Gallant
Tony Gardiner
Sky Gough
Elizabeth Gray
Connor Greig
Stephen Lamberton
Isla McLachlan
Kyl Midgley
Stephen Renton
Darren Riddell
Tiegan Ritchie
Danielle White
David Whitefield
Fraser Wilson